A SAMPLER OF NATIONAL SCIENCE EDUCATION STANDARDS

2002 Edition

National Academy of Sciences,
National Research Council

Includes web links and information about the
National Science Teachers Association

Extracts and Commentary by Joseph M. Peters
University of West Florida

Merrill
Prentice Hall

Upper Saddle River, New Jersey
Columbus, Ohio

All National Science Education Standards quotations are printed with permission from the National Science Education Standards © 1996, National Academy of Sciences, courtesy of the National Academy Press, Washington, D.C.

Complete copies of the National Research Council's National Science Education Standards may be ordered on-line at http://www.nap.edu/readingroom/books/nses/ or by using the form included on the following page of this sampler.

Text design: Darlene Peters

Technical review: Carol Briscoe and Craig Jones, University of West Florida and George O'Brien, Florida International University

Various clipart © 1994, Corel Corporation, *Corel Draw*

Merrill
Prentice Hall

10 9 8 7 6 5 4 3
ISBN: 0-13-041365-8

ORDER FORM

To order the full version of *National Science Education Standards*, photocopy and return to: NATIONAL ACADEMY PRESS, 2101 Constitution Avenue, NW, Lockbox 285, Washington, DC 20055 (Please Print); OR to order by phone, call toll-free 1-800-624-6242

Quantity	ISBN	Title	Price
_____	0-309-05326-9	National Science Education Standards	$19.95

Subtotal _____

Residents of CA, DC, FL, MD, MO, TX and Canada:
Please add applicable sales tax or GST _____

Shipping and Handling: In the U.S. and Canada please add $4.00 for the first book ordered and $0.50 for each additional book. In Australia and New Zealand please add $7.00 for the first book ordered and $1.00 for each additional book. _____

Total _____

____ Payment Enclosed (check or money order payable to National Academy Press)

____ Bill to:
____ Master Card ____ Visa ____ American Express

_____ Expires _____

Signature _____

Phone Number (____) _____

Name _____

Street Address _____

_____

City _____ State ____ ZIP _____
SF97

____ Send me a complete catalog of all National Academy Press books.

____ Send announcements on individual National Academy Press books as they are published.

To join our e-mail notification service, go to the National Academy Press Web site at http://www.nap.edu/fresh/listform.html

INTRODUCTION

In December 1995, the National Academy of Sciences, through its operations branch the National Research Council, released the *National Science Education Standards*, a report designed to guide the country in the improvement of education in the sciences. The *Science Standards*, as they are commonly called, define the content that all of our students should know and understand, as well as the skills students should be capable of performing if they are to be scientifically literate. The developers of the document surrounded the standard for content knowledge with additional standards in science for teaching, professional development, assessment, program development and school system support. Thus, the *Science Standards* represent a bold and robust statement of what it will take to produce graduates of our K-12 system of education who are scientifically literate—citizens who are able to make personal decisions in the area of science and technology and to participate fully in a democratic society. As such, the *Science Standards* are set apart from other documents and reports which are more narrowly constructed.

The *Science Standards*, indeed the entire Standards movement, may have had its birth with another seminal educational document, *A Nation at Risk,* released in 1983 by then Secretary of Education Terrence Bell. Ironically, Terry Bell had been appointed by President Reagan and given the agenda to dismantle the U. S. Department of Education. Instead, *A Nation at Risk* warned us that we were being overcome by a "rising tide of mediocrity." We were, by some accounts, in need of national guidance, for education was seen as a right of all our young citizens. Moreover, education was depicted as an essential vehicle for enabling America to achieve a level of literacy that would ensure productive citizens who in turn would contribute to an economically strong America.

In the mid-1980s, the American Association for the Advancement of Science (AAAS) initiated Science For All Americans (sometimes called Project 2061) and the National Council of Mathematics Teachers, collaborating with the National Research Council, initiated discussions and work which would eventually yield the *Mathematics Standards* in 1989. In the late 1980s, then President Bush convened the country's governors for an educational summit out of which came a set of goals for America to achieve by the year 2000, known as Goals 2000. In science, the National Association of Science Teachers, under the leadership of President Bonnie Brunkhorst, formed committees and discussion groups aimed at identifying science standards. The federal Department of Education funded the National Center for Improving Science Education (NCISE), which over three years (1990-93) produced a series of seminal reports that summarized the research and best ideas for improving elementary, middle level, and high school science. Clearly, the science education communities had launched a standards development effort parallel to that of the mathematics community just a few years earlier. The final piece came into play when the National Research Council took on the responsibility for coordinating the development of the science standards and its subsequent release in December 1995.

The work of the NRC on the standards was supported by several federal agencies: the National Science Foundation, the U.S. Department of Education, the National Aeronautics and Space Administration, and the National Institutes of Health. Yet the *Science Standards* represent the views of thousands of people concerned about science education: scientists, teachers of science (K-16), science teacher educators, school administrators, and parents, as well as many other experts, who share a common vision that we must improve the level of scientific literacy among our youth. Much of the work of developing the standards was accomplished through three working groups, one each for content, assessment, and teaching. Each of the three groups was composed of about 17 members, who were nominated nationally in a blind process and then selected by the National Research Council with the advice of a national advisory committee. The advisory committee, representing diverse interests in science and science education, oversaw the entire four-year developmental process. The final writing stages were guided by the Executive Writing Committee, members drawn largely from the three working groups. Early drafts were widely circulated, and finally a complete draft was published and disseminated for critical review in late 1994. Over 40,000 copies of that draft were circulated and countless focus groups met across the country to provide the NRC with important and significant input on the final version. The *Science Standards* represent the highest quality thinking about science education this country can provide its citizens. Truly, they are *national* in development and consensus and represent a coherent vision of what it means to be scientifically literate.

Importantly, the *Science Standards* lay out recommendations for how we might accomplish this challenging and difficult task, for it is necessary but insufficient to describe what our youth must know, understand, and be able to do in science. Thus, the *Science Standards* begin with a vision for teaching and learning–a vision that reflects the way that science is practiced. Bruce Alberts, President of the National Academy of Sciences, states the case well: "Science is something you do, not something that is done to you." Science learning is an active process in which students observe and describe events and objects, read and seek information through a variety of sources, ask questions, and make hypotheses, carry out investigations, and propose explanations. Science, appropriately taught, seems to be the perfect medium for helping students not only gain important science content knowledge, but also develop communication skills and critical thinking abilities.

It is the *Science Standards* vision for teaching and learning that sets the foundation for the remainder of the recommendations and standards, including those for science content. The standards insist on a level of science literacy that goes well beyond simple science knowledge to science conceptual understanding and application of that knowledge. They recognize that citizens need a high level of literacy in the sciences to engage in decision making around science and science-related issues, to participate in civic and cultural affairs, and to be economically productive. Furthermore, scientific literacy develops over time, including after formal schooling, so the standards represent expectations for all citizens. Inquiry is a significant category among the eight that the *Science Standards* identify and describe, for it is treated not only as a means of teaching and learning, but as a content field. The other categories include unifying concepts and processes, physical science, life science, earth and space science, science and technology, science in personal and social perspectives, and, finally, the history and nature of science. Later in this handbook, the author gives a compact explanation of each and how they might look when they are applied by teachers in classrooms.

How are science learning and content assessed? The *Science Standards* set forth criteria for judging progress of students, teachers, programs, and policies in supporting the implementation of science standards. Ultimately, teaching and testing cannot be separated–they are integral to effective instruction. Assessments then must also align with teaching and with content. Failure to align these three components of science education will result in less than satisfactory results for our students. The assessment standards help all of us think differently about what to assess, when to do so, and how to best determine what students are learning. If we want our students to be able to achieve higher levels of knowledge, conceptual understandings, and abilities to apply that knowledge, assessments must mirror those goals. Failure to improve and diversify standard and non-standard forms of assessments will hinder our youth in becoming more scientifically literate.

Textbook companies and all others who develop and disseminate science curricula bear an important role in the implementation of the *Science Standards*. For too long, we have carried with us a narrow view of science curricula as the content of science. The two are not the same. It is important to note that curricula are developed in light of the standards. More important to curriculum developers is the notion that good content cannot be presented separately from effective teaching and competent assessment. Ultimately, however, the teacher bears

Sampler of National Science Education Standards

responsibility for implementing the curricula and assuring the public that students in their charge have had ample opportunities to learn. Students need multiple and varied ways to experience curricula. And curricula must center on important, standards-based content through instruction that is in keeping with the inquiry standards for learning set forth by the *Science Standards* and assessed through quality approaches that inform their instructional decision making and which also give teachers and others sound guidance regarding what students know, understand, and are able to do in the sciences.

The challenges facing our country's teachers are enormous. While they bear a special responsibility for assuring the public that students achieve the high levels of scientific literacy demanded by the *Science Standards,* we know that full implementation demands that teachers are adequately supported in their development and work. Thus the *Science Standards* chose to include standards for professional development, science programs, and school systems. Becoming an effective teacher is a continuous process beginning with preservice preparation (some would argue it starts even earlier!) and extending through a teacher's professional career. If we are concerned that our K-12 students have adequate and varied opportunities to learn, shouldn't we demand and provide the same for our teachers? Just as students must achieve high levels of science literacy, teachers must have a deep understanding of the content they teach. They, too, must actively learn that content and be involved in an education that builds on their current knowledge, encourages on-going reflection, and supports collaboration among other teachers. They need multiple experiences that connect content with pedagogy, model effective ways of teaching and learning, and use inquiry, reflection, research, modeling, and guided practice.

Sound professional development is not enough. In order for all students to learn, teachers must be familiar with programs that are comprehensive and coordinated. The *Science Standards* provide program standards that will help schools and districts translate the standards into effective programs that reflect local policies and contexts. Such quality programs are likely coordinated with mathematics, have adequate materials and other resources to support the work of teachers, and are structured in ways that provide equitable opportunities for student achievement. These programs allow teachers to implement a curriculum that includes all the content standards, is developmentally appropriate, stresses understanding through inquiry, and connects science to other subjects. Remember that the *Science Standards* are not a curriculum but rather a set of criteria for establishing a curriculum framework that guides states, districts, schools, and teachers.

Finally, the *Science Standards* set forth system standards that call upon all parts of the educational system to coordinate their efforts and build upon each other's strengths. These standards serve as criteria for judging how well the entire system is providing the necessary financial and intellectual resources. Even if all of the other standards are being addressed, failure in this component might mean that necessary policies, consistent with the vision of the *Science Standards,* are not available and all might flounder. Moreover, there needs to be policy coordination across systems—federal, state, and local—if our youth are to achieve the recommended high levels of scientific literacy.

The challenges set forth by the *National Science Education Standards* are substantial. The changes they require will take us well into this century. All of us must be involved in their implementation. This *Sampler* is intended to help the readers know, understand, and implement the standards. Nothing could be more detrimental to improving science education, and the concomitant improvement of science literacy of our youth, than to trivialize the development of *Standards*-based programs. I urge you to read the *Sampler* carefully, to make annotations freely, and to discuss frequently with colleagues and others the rich recommendations contained herein.

Paul J. Kuerbis, Ph.D.
Professor of Education,
The Colorado College and
Member, Teaching Working Group
The *National Science Education Standards*

ORGANIZATION AND NEED FOR THE STANDARDS

What is a Standard and Why Are They Important?
Why Were the National Science Education Standards Developed?
How Are the National Science Education Standards Organized?
What is the Role of Teachers?
What Principles Guided the Development of the Standards?
What are the Goals for Science Education in the Schools?
What do the NSES Mean to You as a Teacher?

ORGANIZATION AND NEED FOR THE STANDARDS

What is a Standard and Why Are They Important?

The use of a *standard* originates with the military. Military standards are conspicuous objects—usually flags or banners—which are attached on top of a pole and used as a rallying point or guide for troops to follow. Similarly, the *National Science Education Standards* (NSES) are a guide to scientific literacy. They provide a central view of where to go to meet the national science education goals. Just as troops follow the guidon, or standard, students, teachers, and the professional education community are challenged to follow the *NSES*. Standards drive what students learn in the classroom and after many years of dismal educational results, the science education community felt it was important to develop standards to guide the reform efforts.

Why Were the National Science Education Standards Developed?

The *National Science Education Standards* document begins with an important *Call to Action* by Bruce Alberts, President of the National Academy of Sciences and Richard Klausner, Chairman of the National Committee on Science Education Standards and Assessment. In the *Call*, the authors sum up the need for science education standards as they discuss the national goal to achieve scientific literacy for all Americans. They state how the *NSES* will help America achieve scientific literacy by providing a framework for teaching and learning which is consistent to the way that science is done by scientists. Drs. Alberts and Klausner also introduce the widespread impact on the educational system which will have to occur in order for the scientific literacy vision to become a reality. Cognizant that this effort may take a long time, they call for dramatic changes in the way science is taught in classrooms. They also identify the many people who will be involved in this change. These key players coincide with chapters of the standards, ranging in scope from the individual student to science education systems in general.

Notice that as you read this *NSES* sampler, the scientific literacy theme becomes evident throughout the text. This should not come as a surprise to anyone since this is a common theme between teachers, school district administrators, business community executives, college and university science educators, scientists, informal science educators, and governmental leaders. In fact, the *NSES* are reflective of the ongoing effort of the American Association for the Advancement of Science (AAAS) *Project 2061, Benchmarks for Science Literacy*, and *Blueprints for Reform* initiatives. Scientific literacy is vital to everyone's future, especially when we consider that a large percentage of future jobs will involve technological applications, the ability to problem solve and think creatively, and the need to use advanced scientific skills to compete in the global workplace.

How Are the National Science Education Standards Organized?

The *NSES* are organized into six chapters which include the standards and two support chapters. Of the six standards chapters, two are related to students' content/process knowledge and assessment of this knowledge, two are related to teaching and teacher professional development, one is devoted to program standards, and one chapter outlines system standards. Specifically, there are chapters relating to the following:

Student Content Standards,
Student Assessment Standards,
Science Teaching Standards,
Professional Development Standards,
Program Standards, and
System Standards.

You will find that the individual student is at the heart of the *NSES*. As such, the standards should be seen as minimum indicators of success, something that every student can and should achieve. Every student should understand the content and be able to perform the scientific skills as they complete the final grade level for their specific grade range. These ranges include Kindergarten through Grade 4, Grades 5-8, and Grades 9-12, each with developmentally-appropriate content standards.

Assessment practices are also specified in the *NSES*. Teachers who follow content and assessment recommendations are assured that the content and skills are evaluated in meaningful ways and are consistent with what is required of students to achieve scientific literacy.

What is the Role of Teachers?

Teachers are seen as a critical component in achieving scientific literacy. It is self evident that the *NSES* need to be *both* a top down (federal, state, and/or school district level) and bottom-up (individual classroom teacher) initiative in order for them to be effective. There are two important sets of standards for the classroom teachers. First, there are the Science Teaching Standards which discuss how to plan, implement, and assess scientific experiences. These are the standards which promote inquiry-based or active learning as opposed to rote memorization of scientific definitions. Second, there are the Professional Development Standards which discuss how the teacher can become more confident in teaching science through lifelong learning, and the development of meaningful understandings of scientific concepts and the nature of science.

The Teaching and Professional Development Standards work together to address the notion of achieving *pedagogical content knowledge,* or the ability to integrate knowledge of science; knowledge of the learning process; knowledge of effective teaching methods; knowledge of students' developmental levels; knowledge of the educational aims, goals, and objectives; and knowledge of the curriculum into classroom activities. The teacher-related standards also speak to teacher facilitation of the positive learning environment which should occur in the classroom. This environment enables students to be successful in science experiences and promotes positive feelings toward future science learning both in the classroom and throughout life.

At the other end of the educational spectrum are the Science Education Program Standards and the Science Education System Standards. Individual teachers cannot achieve scientific literacy for all students if they are in an isolated classroom or in a school or school system which does not recognize the importance of this effort. Therefore, the *NSES* define the needed concurrence between the content standards, the school's curriculum, district goals and state or federal policies. The coherence among curriculum developers, policy makers, funding sources, and assessment scenarios is vital to the success of each student as they progress through the system. What is taught has to be in line with what is assessed; what is taught and assessed has to be congruent with the curriculum, and the curriculum has to match district and state initiatives in order to provide resources for continued teaching. Likewise, professional development has to correspond to

What Principles Guided the Development of the Standards?

Before all of the groups involved in establishing the *NSES* undertook the task of identifying the standards, they first had to establish some ground rules. As in the past, there were differing perspectives on what was the best way to achieve scientific literacy for America's workforce. However, the importance of scientific literacy for America's future was common ground. This is evident in the tremendous effort to bring together various voices to a common understanding in the *NSES*. From the U.S. Department of Education, nearly every scientific and science education organization, school district officials, to individual teachers, had a chance to provide input into the final document. There were over 40,000 copies of the draft document sent out for comment and revision before the *NSES* document was finalized. Discussion on educational reform, learning theory, and culture led to establishing common principles. These principles are defined in the *NSES* as follows:

science is for all students,

learning science is an active process,

school science reflects the intellectual and cultural traditions that characterize the practice of contemporary science,

and improving science is part of systematic educational reform.

Reprinted with permission from the National Science Education Standards ©1996, National Academy of Sciences, courtesy of the National Academy Press, Washington, D.C. (p. 19).

Equity, excellence, and inclusion issues guide the *science for all* principle. Each student is able to achieve scientific literacy and should be provided the opportunity to excel in the classroom. Every child, including underachieving, gifted, culturally diverse, and challenged populations, are able to benefit from the inquiry promoted through the *NSES* content standards.

The idea that learning science is something students should *do,* not something that should be done to them, reinforces the *science for all* precept. The content standards are written in the context of inquiry where hands-on/minds-on activities, critical thinking, and learning science as a scientific endeavor are promoted This reinforces the *learning science is an active process* principle.

The nature of science, what is–and is not–science, and the interaction of culture and science are characteristic of the next principle. The strong influence of the science-technology-society interaction is evident. Understanding that scientific research leads to technological breakthroughs which are funded through, and used by society, as well as how technology leads to further scientific discovery is included in this principle.

Finally, interplay of students, teachers, principals, superintendents, school board members, university education professors, textbook publishers, parents, industry, businesses, scientists, government officials, and informal science educators all play a part in the principle of *improving science is part of systematic educational reform*. The history of scientific reform teaches us that we will need long-term systematic reform in order to achieve the vision of the *NSES*.

What are the Goals for Science Education in the Schools?

As you may already see, there was a consensus as to the need, organization, and content of the *NSES*. One might ask how a consensus was possible, given the diversity among all of the groups involved. As with the aforementioned principles, the answer to this question lies in the common goals for science education. In the *NSES* document, these *Goals for School Science* are defined in terms of the students' ability to:

experience the richness and excitement of knowing about and understanding the natural world;

use appropriate scientific processes and principles in making personal decisions;

engage intellectually in public discourse and debate about matters of scientific and technological concern;

and increase their economic productivity through the use of knowledge, understanding, and skills of the scientifically literate person in their careers.

Reprinted with permission from the National Science Education Standards ©1996, National Academy of Sciences, courtesy of the National Academy Press, Washington, D.C. (p. 13).

These goals are the self-evident desires of our society. We want adults who, after completing the three levels of scientific learning, are still eager to learn more about the natural and designed world. We also want adults who can take positions on issues based on informed personal decision. They should be able to provide for their offspring, because they have developed the necessary skills to compete in the global workforce and the explosive technological and information-based world. The goals also call for workers who possess the ability to think independently, as a team member, logically, and creatively as they complete the challenges of employment and everyday life.

In summary, the *NSES* became the vehicle for the shared vision of the many voices concerned with science education.

What do the *NSES* Mean to You as a Teacher?

As you read through the remainder of this booklet, keep in mind that the standards were written with you in mind. Therefore, they are flexible enough for you to adapt to your professional development and classroom needs. They will supplement, replace, or guide the established science curriculum or provide a new way of teaching concepts. The *NSES* also provide support for why you would teach science

through inquiry or want to become more active in your school's curriculum development. Finally, they provide a resource when you look for support for your own science education program.

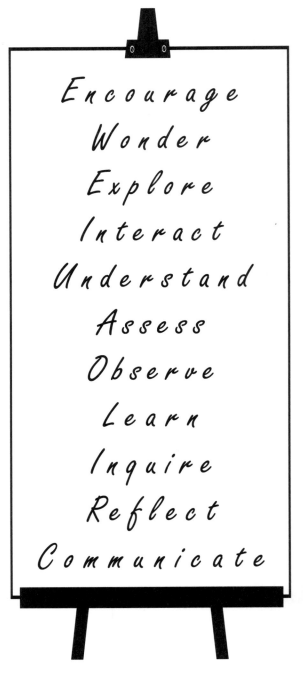

Encourage
Wonder
Explore
Interact
Understand
Assess
Observe
Learn
Inquire
Reflect
Communicate

SCIENCE TEACHING STANDARDS

What Role Do Teachers Play in the Learning Process?

The National Science Education Teaching Standards are considered by many as the most important of the *NSES*. This is because teachers are the key to planning, implementation, and assessment of the science activities which will allow us to achieve the vision of a scientifically-literate citizenship. This is not to say that the entire reform effort should rest on the individual efforts of teachers. Rather, it is the specific teacher who needs our support as he or she plans, facilitates learning, assesses his or her teaching, assesses student learning, manages all aspects of the classroom, promotes learning communities, and develops programs.

Parents, administrators, policy makers, and business leaders need to understand the complexity of the classroom and work in cooperation with teachers to encourage the day-to-day inquiry necessary for success in science. Specifically, they need to understand and apply the five assumptions from which the Teaching Standards were developed.

Five Assumptions Provided by the *NSES*.

The *NSES* document provides the following five assumptions for science teaching.

The vision of science education described by the NSES requires changes throughout the entire system.

What students learn is greatly influenced by how they are taught.

The actions of teachers are deeply influenced by their perceptions of science as an enterprise and as a subject to be taught and learned.

Student understanding is actively constructed through individual and social processes.

Actions of teachers are deeply influenced by their understanding of and relationships with students.

Reprinted with permission from the National Science Education Standards ©1996, National Academy of Sciences, courtesy of the National Academy Press, Washington, D.C. (p. 28).

First, the vision of science education must work toward a long-term change in the way science is taught in our classrooms. Many district-level, state-wide, and even national quick-fix programs in the past had failed because they were reactionary and not based on a future vision of what was needed for sustained change. Others were top-down approaches which were left for teachers to implement without any resources or classroom support. They did not include teachers in the process but expected teachers to be able to successfully carry them out in their classrooms. Rarely has any program involving systematic change had all of the stakeholders involved to the extent that the *NSES* has.

In consideration of principle number two, we must understand that teachers influence the learning of students on a daily basis. Each time an educator makes a decision about what is taught, how it is taught, to whom it is taught, and why it is taught, the students respond in kind.

Put another way, the professional teacher needs to know the developmental level, interests, and abilities of students as well as the content of science. Then, through effective planning, she or he can amalgamate student needs, scientific content, and cultural needs through the mediation of a standards-based curriculum. This means putting all of the pieces together in a coherent manner to provide the best possible opportunity to learn and to assess learning.

The effectiveness of the second assumption is, for the most part, based on the third assumption concerning teacher beliefs. In order to have a real impact in the classroom, teachers must first examine their own beliefs and understandings before entering the classroom. You cannot expect a teacher who is afraid to learn science along with students to be effective at teaching an unfamiliar concept. This is especially true if the teacher has not had positive science learning experiences in the past or has had a program of memorization-only science. Teachers must understand the nature of science and its importance in the students' knowledge base.

Related to the need to teach science is the obvious need to teach it well. Science is an active search for answers and understandings. Scientific knowledge is constructed through inquiry and the cultural exchange of questions and discussions. The *Standards* are based on learning scientific concepts through inquiry.

A final assumption is the need for teachers to understand the needs and backgrounds of their students. Every student can be a challenge for the teacher and yet, every student can succeed if teachers are committed to success for all students in their classroom. The following standards will further define the role of the teacher in the vision for a scientifically-literate society.

Teaching Standard A–Planning.
Teachers of science plan an inquiry-based science program for their students. In doing this, teachers:

Develop a framework of yearlong and short-term goals for students.

Select science content and adapt and design curricula to meet the interests, knowledge, understanding, abilities, and experiences of students.

Select teaching and assessment strategies that support the development of student understanding and nurture a community of science learners.

Work together as colleagues within and across disciplines and grade levels.

Reprinted with permission from the National Science Education Standards ©1996, National Academy of Sciences, courtesy of the National Academy Press, Washington, D.C. (p. 30).

Most student teaching supervisors will mentor the preservice teachers on the need for effective planning. After all, it is the planning that provides the framework for transforming the teacher's personal understanding of science content and the teaching process into effective learning situations for their students. The classroom leader must work within time limitations, diverse student needs, and school-based science programs when developing strategies. Often times, planning will become part of the actual lesson as teachers involve students. Planning should be both a teacher responsibility and a normal part of the classroom activities as in Standard B.

Teaching Standard B–Guide and Facilitate Learning.

Teachers of science guide and facilitate learning. In doing this, teachers:

Focus and support inquiries while interacting with students.

Orchestrate discourse among students about scientific ideas.

Challenge students to accept and share responsibility for their own learning.

Recognize and respond to student diversity and encourage all students to participate fully in science learning.

Encourage and model the skills of scientific inquiry, as well as the curiosity, openness to new ideas and data, and skepticism that characterize science.

The influence of constructivism has brought about revolutionary new ways of teaching. Radical constructivism based on Ernst von Glasersfeld's (1989) research and social constructivism based on the writings of Lev Vygotsky (1962) are two approaches to thinking about how students actively construct knowledge based on prior knowledge. They also provide guidelines for active learning.

The implications of constructivism are far reaching. For instance, teachers must assess prior knowledge before proceeding with a new concept, they must help students make meaningful connections between the new content and what students already understand, and teachers will have to involve students in an active learning environment. One approach is the use of *KWL* or *Know, Want* to know, and *Learned*. This strategy begins with teachers allowing students to write on a markerboard or posterboard what they know about a topic. Next, the students put down what they want to find out about the topic. Students then explore the topic and then write down what they learned as well as new questions. Another effective strategy is to use concept mapping. Novak and Gowin (1984) and others have found this to be a very effective way to assess students before and after a lesson. It is supportive of the constructivist philosophy and promotes discourse with and among students.

Teaching Standard C–Assessment.

Teachers of science engage in ongoing assessment of their teaching and of student learning. In doing this, teachers:

Use multiple methods and systematically gather data about student understanding and ability.

Analyze assessment data to guide teaching.

Guide students in self-assessment.

Use student data, observations of teaching, and interactions with colleagues to reflect on and improve teaching practice.

Use student data, observations of teaching, and interactions with colleagues to report student achievement and opportunities to learn to students, teachers, parents, policy makers, and the general public.

Although assessment has a separate set of standards in the *NSES,* it is important to reinforce the linkage between teaching standards and assessment. Teachers must consistently find out what students know and are capable of learning if they are to be efficient at analyzing their own teaching. The teacher needs to look at what works in his or her classroom and build on these strengths and his or her student's strengths. The assessment is also an important part of looking at programs and systems to see if they are functioning properly or in need of some adjustment.

Teaching Standard D–Learning Environments.

Teachers of science design and manage learning environments that provide students with the time, space, and resources needed for learning science. In doing this, teachers:

Structure the time available so that students are able to engage in extended investigations.

Create a setting for student work that is flexible and supportive of science inquiry.

Ensure a safe working environment.

Make the available science tools, materials, media, and technological resources accessible to students.

Identify and use resources outside the school.

Engage students in designing the learning environment.

One thing that teachers will notice about this approach to teaching is that it is very time consuming. It is important though, to take the time to foster inquiry and promote discourse with students. It is not enough to do a *magic show* demonstration or *cookbook* lab. The follow up discourse is essential in identifying misconceptions and promoting further inquiry. Teaching fewer concepts but teaching them better, i.e. follow-up discussions and extending investigations, is one theme of the current reform movement.

A powerful tool in creating student-centered, inquiry-based learning is cooperative or collaborative learning. Cooperative learning is seen as dividing tasks into smaller pieces and having each group member work on one of the parts. Collaborative learning is two or more students working together to find a joint solution to a problem (Linn & Burbules, 1993). The use of student teams to assist in preparing for and cleaning up after activities will help to provide more time for the actual inquiry and follow-up discourse. One suggestion is to use cooperative learning teams with a team leader, materials manager, maintenance manager, secretary, and liaison as in the Inquiry Task Group Management System (Jones, 1990). This gives each student a specific task which will keep them engaged. Tasks can be rotated with a classroom schedule and groups can be rotated based on gender, achievement level, or science attitudes.

Teaching Standard E–Communities of Learners.

Teachers of science develop *communities of science learners* that reflect the intellectual rigor of scientific inquiry and the attitudes and social values conducive to science learning. In doing this, teachers:

Display and demand respect for the diverse ideas, skills, and experiences of all students.

Enable students to have a significant voice in decisions about the content and context of their work and require students to take responsibility for the learning of all members of the community.

Nurture collaboration among students.

Structure and facilitate ongoing formal and informal discussion based on a shared understanding of rules of scientific discourse.

Model and emphasize the skills, attitudes, and values of scientific inquiry.

Communities of learners are seen as a place where there is "the continuous generation and exchange of knowledge, a process made possible by our inherent desire and capacity for new learning" (Marshall, 1997). These communities are beneficial in developing literacy and communication skills. The communities should begin at elementary school and continue throughout graduate school. Most elementary students are very excited about learning-- especially science. Later, as they move into middle school, some thing happens to discourage the students from their natural curiosity. By high school, most students only want to do the minimum science needed to graduate. Many explanations are offered for this phenomena but one important reason is that students become tired of memorizing science vocabulary and orally reading the text. They want to explore their natural world and seek answers to the phenomena they see. We as science teachers need to foster this interaction with the environment and build communities of learners who will continue to explore throughout life.

Some of the challenges in building the community are stereotypes, language, and cultural differences. Students often have very negative views of a scientist. They do not want to be seen as a scientist or even associate with one of them. Gender also plays a role here. Science is often seen as something only for boys. Arranging female-only learning groups and consciously calling on females will help to change this. Teachers can also change this view by offering many examples of scientists in the community, including female and minority scientists.

Language is another deterrent in effective science. Most science textbooks have more new terms and concepts than a grade equivalent foreign language text. Each teacher begins with teaching the definitions in isolation hoping the next teacher will apply what is learned. Unfortunately, most teachers do not go beyond the definitions since they feel that they need to cover everything in the book. By teaching only select topics and studying them in more depth, students will develop a real understanding of the material. Language considerations are also critical in culturally-diverse classrooms. The language used in science may have a different meaning for students of Spanish, Native American, African or others of non-Anglo descent.

Teaching Standard F–Planning and Development.

Teachers of science actively participate in the ongoing planning and development of the school science program. In doing this, teachers:

Plan and develop the school science program.

Participate in decisions concerning the allocation of time and other resources to the science program.

Participate fully in planning and implementing professional growth and development strategies for themselves and their colleagues.

Reprinted with permission from the National Science Education Standards ©1996, National Academy of Sciences, courtesy of the National Academy Press, Washington, D.C. (p. 51).

Teachers need to work together to support communities of learners within a school. The faculty need to support each others' innovations and be willing to try out new ideas such as integrated curriculum, hands-on/minds-on science, and problem-centered activities. There are many resources available for teachers who are looking for new ideas. For example, the National Science Teachers Association is producing the *Pathways to the Science Standards* documents (1996, 1997). The National Science Resources Center is also developing materials such as the *Science for All Children* book (1997).

Summary of the Teaching Standards.

The *Standards* call for changes in the way science is taught in our classrooms. In summary they seek to change the way science is taught through more emphasis on the following:

Understanding and responding to individual student's interests, strengths, experiences, and needs.

Selecting and adapting curriculum.

Focusing on student understanding and use of scientific knowledge, ideas, and inquiry processes.

Guiding students in active and extended scientific inquiry.

Providing opportunities for scientific discussion and debate among students.

Continuously assessing student understanding.

Sharing responsibility for learning with students.

Supporting a classroom community with cooperation, shared responsibility, and respect.

Working with other teachers to enhance the science program.

The changing emphasis reflects the strong influence of the constructivist philosophy which encourages teachers to do things differently in the classroom. One difference is in teaching. For the most part, teachers will teach differently than they were taught themselves. They will focus on the learning of scientific knowledge and skills for their students. These will be learned in the same manner as science is explored by scientists, instead of memorization of numerous disjointed facts and definitions. A deeper understanding of a few important concepts will result. These concepts are integrated into the entire school curriculum and build on each other in an upward spiral. Consequently, as teachers plan, guide, and assess students, they will have to remember that they are the most important component of the educational system. They are the primary force for true reform.

Linda's Teaching Situation

Linda is an elementary teacher with seven years experience. She teaches in an urban public school. Her school has recently established a school-wide Advisory Council to support educational reform. The council is made up of teachers, parents, the school principal, and community representatives. They are the governing body for funding and curriculum issues at the school. Tonight, Linda is representing the fourth grade teachers as she seeks council support to change the science curriculum taught at that grade level in her school. She begins by announcing that:

The fourth grade teachers recently attended sessions at the National Science Teachers Association meeting where the National Science Education Standards were being discussed. All of the fourth grade teachers agree that the school should rethink what has been occurring in their classrooms. The fourth grade teachers want the council to redirect the purchase of new science textbooks in favor of some inexpensive kitchen chemistry equipment which can be used for scientific inquiry in their classrooms. Furthermore, the teachers want to redesign the science curriculum to align with the NSES.

Wes, a spokesperson for many parents is immediately inquisitive as to what effect this would have on the standardized tests at the school since they had always been above average. Bill, another parent expresses concern over what this will mean to students preparing for the grade five science program. Janet, the principal, questions how this will affect other parts of the curriculum since they had been placing a large emphasis on the reading and mathematics achievement scores the past two years.

Linda pauses to reflect on what to say to the group. Before she has a chance to speak, support for the teachers' idea is initiated from the business representative who owns a small company. Priscilla expresses that she would encourage the change since it would "promote independent thinking and a desire to learn more with the children—something desperately needed in today's workforce." She goes on to state that her company has to keep sending workers away for training since they lack the skills which would be promoted through this type of curriculum and that the standardized tests do not effectively identify the workers she needs.

Doris, a parent representative and high school teacher, provides further justification. She states that with the tremendous amount of information available, teachers could not possibly teach everything. The other teachers at the high school shared the opinion that inquiry skills are much more important to success in the sciences than what is currently being taught at the elementary school.

Sue, a third grade teacher addresses the group and comments on how there does not have to be a reduction in math or reading since the teachers can integrate science into these areas. Children's literature can be the springboard for units of study in many areas related to science. She noted that with her weather unit, children wrote stories, kept weather charts, compared temperatures, downloaded weather information on the Internet, and read many stories related to weather. These activities were supportive of math and reading.

Linda's proposal is overwhelmingly accepted by the group. They ask her to report back in a few months to see how things are going.

purchase of new science textbooks in favor of some inexpensive kitchen chemistry equipment/redesign the science curriculum to align with the NSES

STANDARDS FOR PROFESSIONAL DEVELOPMENT FOR TEACHERS OF SCIENCE

Are Changes Needed in Professional Development Programs?

As professionals, teachers need the same ongoing development as doctors, lawyers, certified public accountants, or engineers. Teachers need the opportunity to keep up with new scientific discoveries, best practices or methodologies for teaching, and new resources which are available for their classroom.

Professional development is a life-long process. In a life-saving situation, you would not want to go to a doctor who is using the procedures that were available when he or she went to medical school 30 years ago, or the same hospital equipment that was available when it was built 50 years ago. Yet, if we were to compare the teaching or classroom of today with one from years back, we would find that basically little has changed. Despite the fact that the nation is no longer agricultural, or even heavily industrial, we still employ the educational support of generations past. Today's technologically complex and information-based workplace needs workers who can problem solve, work with technology, and learn new concepts independently. In order for this to happen, teachers must first undergo meaningful professional development to both understand the situation and to be able to adapt their teaching accordingly. The *NSES* provide some assumptions for this.

Four Professional Development Assumptions based on the *NSES*.

Assumptions about the nature of professional development experiences and about the context within which they take place frame the professional development standards:

Professional development for a teacher of science is a continuous, lifelong process.

The traditional distinctions between "targets", "sources", and "supporters" of teacher development activities are artificial.

The conventional view of professional development for teachers needs to shift from technical training for specific skills to opportunities for intellectual professional growth.

The process of transforming schools requires that professional development opportunities be clearly and appropriately connected to teachers' work in the context of the school.

A common theme which runs throughout the professional development standards is that teachers need to experience good science as part their inservice. They have to be taught scientific concepts through inquiry much like their students will need to learn scientific concepts through inquiry. Programs such as the Triangle Coalition's *Scientific Work Experiences for Teachers* (SWEPT) program or some National Science Foundation funded summer workshops allow teachers to work with scientists to receive this much needed professional development. The emphasis is not primarily on content but on developing scientific skills and content through inquiry.

Teachers *teach as they were taught* is a common saying. The first standard of professional development is about learning, since we want teachers to learn, and later, teach science consistent with the nature of science and inquiry.

Professional Development Standard A– Science Learning.

Professional development for teachers of science requires learning essential science content through the perspectives and methods of inquiry. Science learning experiences for teachers must:

Involve teachers in actively investigating phenomena that can be studied scientifically, interpreting results, and making sense of findings consistent with currently accepted scientific understanding.

Address issues, events, problems, or topics significant in science and of interest to participants.

Introduce teachers to scientific literature, media, and technological resources that expand their science knowledge and their ability to access further knowledge.

Build on the teacher's current science understanding, ability, and attitudes.

Incorporate ongoing reflection on the process and outcomes of understanding science through inquiry.

Encourage and support teachers in efforts to collaborate.

Reprinted with permission from the National Science Education Standards ©1996, National Academy of Sciences, courtesy of the National Academy Press, Washington, D.C. (p. 59).

There are numerous resources available for professional development including scientific television shows on cable television, scientific newsletters and journals, nationally- or state-funded inservice projects, scientific and science education conferences, and the Internet. Federal Eisenhower funding (Title II) and other grants are another way to develop an inservice plan for a particular team of teachers, school, or district. Teachers should check with their principal or the district's science supervisor for more details.

Collaboration is a key concept for the success of this professional development standard. Teachers who can discuss successes and failures, share new ideas, and plan with other teachers find it more meaningful when they participate in professional development. Later, they find it easier to carry out changes in their classrooms.

Professional Development Standard B– Pedagogical Content Knowledge.

Professional development for teachers of science requires integrating knowledge of science, learning, pedagogy, and students; it also requires applying that knowledge to science teaching. Learning experiences for teachers of science must:

Connect and integrate all pertinent aspects of science and science education.

Occur in a variety of places where effective science teaching can be illustrated and modeled, permitting teachers to struggle with real situations and expand their knowledge and skills in appropriate contexts.

Address teachers' needs as learners and build on their current knowledge of science content, teaching, and learning.

Use inquiry, reflection, interpretation of research, modeling, and guided practice to build understanding and skill in science teaching.

Reprinted with permission from the National Science Education Standards ©1996, National Academy of Sciences, courtesy of the National Academy Press, Washington, D.C. (p. 62).

Lee Shulman (1986, 1987) describes a teacher's pedagogical content knowledge as a second kind of content knowledge. It is a knowledge which is more than ordinary content knowledge such as a chemist or engineer possesses. It also goes beyond the pedagogical knowledge of a beginning teacher. It is knowledge of *subject matter for teaching and* encompasses the most powerful strategies for assisting the students in learning the subject matter. These strategies include effective discourse with students, student-centered inquiry, and teacher-provided analogies, metaphors, and similes. As Professional Development Standard B suggests, professional development should reflect the notion of pedagogical content knowledge and integrate content, pedagogy, knowledge of the curriculum, knowledge of the students and their developmental levels, and knowledge of how students learn.

Reflection is an important aspect of this standard. The constructivist movement has shifted the focus of teachers being technical experts to that of reflective practitioners. This is due to their *construction* of ideas related to their teaching. They constantly form new ideas, teaching strategies, assessment rubrics, and concepts. They test these in the classroom and reflect on their success which leads to new knowledge and methods. This constant learning process is emphasized in Standard C.

Professional Development Standard C– Lifelong Learning.

Professional development for teachers of science requires building understanding and ability for lifelong learning. Professional development activities must:

Provide regular, frequent opportunities for individual and collegial examination and reflection on classroom and institutional practice.

Provide opportunities for teachers to receive feedback about their teaching and to understand, analyze, and apply that feedback to improve their practice.

Provide opportunities for teachers to learn and use various tools and techniques for self-reflection and collegial reflection, such as peer coaching, portfolios, and journals.

Support the sharing of teacher expertise by preparing and using mentors, teacher advisers, coaches, lead teachers, and resource teachers to provide professional development opportunities.

Provide opportunities to know and have access to existing research and experiential knowledge.

Provide opportunities to learn and use the skills of research to generate new knowledge about science and the teaching and learning of science.

Reprinted with permission from the National Science Education Standards ©1996, National Academy of Sciences, courtesy of the National Academy Press, Washington, D.C. (p. 68).

In order for professional development to work, inservice providers and teachers must be willing to complete long-term growth. Often times, this takes the form of assisting the teacher in a year-long, inquiry-based project, an action research study, or a state or nationally-funded science project. Taking ample time to present new information and make connections to the teacher's existing knowledge enhances the teacher's professional knowledge of teaching.

School-wide mentoring programs, teacher-business alliances, teacher-university partnerships, and Internet-mediated discussions are also effective ways of promoting professional development and encouraging lifelong learning.

Certification programs, such as the National Science Teachers Association certification project, and other beginning/ongoing teacher development projects, also make significant contributions to a successful professional development program. Portfolios are an important component of this process since they encourage reflection and self-development. Teachers who participate in developing portfolios are also more inclined to use them with students because they see their value as an assessment tool.

Professional Development Standard D– Quality Inservice.

Professional development programs for teachers of science must be coherent and integrated. Quality preservice and inservice programs are characterized by:

Clear, shared goals based on a vision of science learning, teaching, and teacher development congruent with the National Science Education Standards.

Integration and coordination of the program components so that understanding and ability can be built over time, reinforced continuously, and practiced in a variety of situations.

Options that recognize the developmental nature of teacher professional growth and individual and group interests, as well as the needs of teachers who have varying degrees of experience, professional expertise, and proficiency.

Collaboration among the people involved in programs, including teachers, teacher educators, teacher unions, scientists, administrators, policy makers, members of professional and scientific organizations, parents, and business people, with clear respect for the perspectives and expertise of each.

Recognition of the history, culture, and organization of the school environment.

Continuous program assessment that captures the perspectives of all those involved, uses a variety of strategies, focuses on the process and effects of the program, and feeds directly into program improvement and evaluation.

Reprinted with permission from the National Science Education Standards ©1996, National academy of Sciences, courtesy of the National Academy Press, Washington, D.C. (p. 70).

When developing a professional development program for teachers there is no such thing as a "one size fits all" master plan. Inservice must be developed with the individual teacher, school, and district goals in mind. Shared goals involving all of the stakeholders are much more meaningful to all involved.

Summary of the Professional Development Standards.

The Professional Development standards emphasize inservice which is consistent with inquiry in science and teachers as reflective practitioners. Specifically, there is more emphasis on the following:

Inquiry into teaching and learning.

Learning science through investigation and inquiry.

Integration of science and teaching knowledge.

Integration of theory and practice in school settings.

Collegial and collaborative learning.

Long-term coherent plans.

A variety of professional development activities.

A mix of internal and external expertise.

Staff developers as facilitators, consultants, and planners.

Teacher as intellectual, reflective practitioner.

Teacher as producer of knowledge about teaching.

Teacher as leader.

Teacher as a member of a collegial professional community

Teacher as source and facilitator of change.

Reprinted with permission from the National Science Education Standards ©1996, National Academy of Sciences, courtesy of the National Academy Press, Washington, D.C. (p. 72).

The professional development standards represent a new way of looking at how to view the teaching profession. Teachers are no longer lectured in short to *make and take* sessions. Rather, they are engaged in meaningful inquiry which will contribute to lifelong learning. This can be during workshops, college courses, inservice projects, action research studies, within the scientific workplace, or a variety of other ways. A new sense of professionalism is disclosed in the professional development standards. Teacher-leaders engaging in research and inquiry-based learning to make the classroom environment a better place sums up the shared vision of these standards.

Linda's Professional Development

As we rejoin Linda after a few months of her new standards-based curriculum, we find that she has returned to the Advisory Council in search of support for inservice. She addresses the council, stating that

The fourth grade teachers are so excited about what they are doing that they want to have time to share their programs with the fifth grade teachers who are receptive of the new methods. We would like to have permission to have six early dismissal days during the school year. Three days will be for sharing what we are doing in the classroom and three days will be for planning future units on a grade-level basis.

Support for these ideas was debated briefly among the Council. Janet, the principal, noted that since no days will be missed, or substitutes hired, the inservice plan was acceptable to her. Priscilla, the business representative, added that she would like to see the inservice plan expanded to include the exchange of employees. She hoped that she could send some workers from her manufacturing plant to the school to get an idea of what teaching was all about and how her business could support the teachers' efforts. Likewise, she would invite the teachers to the plant for the day to experience science in the workplace.

> It was agreed that they would try this out twice the following year, as a test, and then expand it with other teachers and businesses if it proved to be beneficial. The parents agreed that they would subsidize the plan from the Parent Teacher Organization fundraisers.

ASSESSMENT STANDARDS

What is Assessment and Why is it Integral to the *NSES?*

Standards are of little value unless there are assessment procedures in place to measure their effectiveness. The *NSES* indicate that assessment is the primary feedback mechanism in the science education system. Note that there is a difference between assessment and evaluation. Evaluation is a judgmental procedure for an individual student. For example, the student makes a graph of the average number of heartbeats before, during, and after exercise. This evaluation procedure will generally lead to a grade or may lead to the teacher planning additional activities if a number of students have poor grades. Assessment, conversely, is more generalized and shows what groups of students know or the skills which they can perform. Assessment helps to see if the entire science education program is working.

What is Authentic Assessment?

Authentic assessment is seen as an assessment procedure which is closely related to actual outcomes of science education. For instance, if the learning activity was to learn to measure length in the metric system, a possible assessment procedure would involve the actual skill of measuring the length of the classroom to compare it to the length of a blue whale. This is opposed to assessing the skill through a multiple choice test which would list four possible answers for the room's length. Authentic assessment is the best example of how assessment and learning are one in the same because, as students are assessed, they should be engaged in learning and vice versa. Authentic assessment supports the standards because of its purpose and close relationship to what is taught.

Assessment Standard A–Clear and Consistent Procedures.

Assessments must be consistent with the decisions they are designed to inform.

Assessments are deliberately designed.

Assessments have explicitly stated purposes.

The relationship between the decisions and the data is clear.

Assessment procedures are internally consistent.

Reprinted with permission from the National Science Education Standards ©1996, National Academy of Sciences, courtesy of the National Academy Press, Washington, D.C. (p. 78).

Consistency is key to Assessment Standard A. Assessment procedures must first be consistent with instruction. Assessment must also be consistent with the impending decisions about the curriculum or instructional practice. Instructional practice, likewise, will also have to be consistent with assessment to give an accurate picture of achievement of the standards. Consequently, teachers need to ask the questions:

Who should be assessed? Would it be better to assess all students, selective students, or the teacher?

What do I hope to learn from this assessment? Will it tell me what students have learned, what they need to learn, or if I have provided an opportunity to learn?

When should this assessment occur? Should I start the activity with an assessment, end the activity with an assessment, or complete assessment throughout the activity?

Where will this assessment be done? Is it better to complete the assessment in the classroom, the laboratory, at home, in the library, or on the computer?

How will this assessment support learning? Is this assessment really necessary to promote present or future learning?

Why do students need this assessment? Is the assessment for comparisons between students implemented to indicate misconceptions, or to provide me with a baseline of what students know?

Assessment Standard B–Achievement and Opportunity to Learn.

Achievement and opportunity to learn science must be assessed.

Achievement data collected focus on the science content that is most important for students to learn.

Opportunity-to-learn data collected focus on the most powerful indicators.

Equal attention must be given to the assessment of opportunity to learn and to the assessment of student achievement.

Reprinted with permission from the National Science Education Standards ©1996, National Academy of Sciences, courtesy of the National Academy Press, Washington, D.C. (p. 79).

With the tremendous rate at which new knowledge is being acquired, it is important to focus on the most meaningful information and skills which students must know. Assessment becomes critical when considering which information and skills are most important. As we assess students there are two considerations - the learner and the opportunity to learn. When the focus is on achievement, the data is used to compare individual students, similar classes, entire schools, school districts, states, and nations. Opportunity to learn, on the other hand, involves what is done to facilitate the learning process. It is much more than an achievement test. It encompasses such things as class time devoted to science learning, the principal's support, school-wide attitude toward science education, the equipment available for science education, and the science curriculum. Students may have an excellent opportunity to learn, develop a variety of important scientific skills, and never do well on a standardized test which does not measure their learning. This leads into the need for authentic assessment or what some educators call *alternative assessment.*

Assessment Standard C–Authentic Assessment.

The technical quality of the data collected is well-matched to the decisions and actions taken on the basis of their interpretation.

The feature that is claimed to be measured is actually measured.

Assessment tasks are authentic.

An individual student's performance is similar on two or more tasks that claim to measure the same aspect of student achievement.

Students have adequate opportunity to demonstrate their achievements.

Assessment tasks and methods of presenting them provide data that are sufficiently stable to lead to the same decisions if used at different times.

Reprinted with permission from the National Science Education Standards ©1996, National Academy of Sciences, courtesy of the National Academy Press, Washington, D.C. (p. 83).

Testing reliability is the ability of a test to produce the same results when given numerous times. Validity is the ability of a test to measure what it should measure. Both reliability and validity are important to the decision making process. For example, if you test a student's ability to form a hypothesis by providing 10 true/false questions which consist of sample hypothesis, there is a 50% chance of the student guessing the correct answers. A much more valid measure would be to provide a sample situation and have the student actually develop his or her own hypothesis. Reliability is maintained by posing several opportunities for students to develop hypothesis throughout the school year. The *NSES* propose the use of authentic assessment since it is congruent with learning and generally has a high level of validity and reliability.

Another important reason for the use of authentic assessment has to do with student learning ability and student diversity. Students learn best when the material is consistent with their developmental level. Since students take the responsibility for authentic assessment tasks, the tasks are generally a good match developmentally. Students are using vocabulary they are familiar with when writing in a journal or completing a portfolio. Standardized tests, on the other hand, can include inappropriate vocabulary for a particular student population. This is also true when we look at minority populations. The students may be very competent in a task, yet unable to express this competence in a multiple choice test because they cannot understand the context due to language differences.

Assessment Standard D–Fair Assessment.
Assessment practices must be fair.

Assessment tasks must be reviewed for the use of stereotypes, for assumptions that reflect the perspectives or experiences of a particular group, for language that might be offensive to a particular group, and for other features that might distract students from the intended task.

Large-scale assessments must use statistical techniques to identify potential bias among subgroups.

Assessment tasks must be appropriately modified to accommodate the needs of students with physical disabilities, learning disabilities, or limited English proficiency.

Assessment tasks must be set in a variety of contexts, be engaging to students with different interests and experiences, and must not assume the perspective or experience of a particular gender, racial, or ethnic group.

Reprinted with permission from the National Science Education Standards ©1996, National Academy of Sciences, courtesy of the National Academy Press, Washington, D.C. (p. 85).

Just as *science is for all,* assessment must be for all. This means that assessment practices must be done in a way that is nondiscriminatory. Generally, the best approach to this is to allow students to *show what they know* through portfolios or journals. These are collections of an individual student's work which are scored by the teacher based on a rubric or predetermined scoring plan.

Assessment Standard–Sound Inferences.
The inferences made from assessments about student achievement and opportunity to learn must be sound.

When making inferences from assessment data about student achievement and opportunity to learn science, explicit reference needs to be made to the assumptions on which the inferences are based.

Reprinted with permission from the National Science Education Standards ©1996, National Academy of Sciences, courtesy of the National Academy Press, Washington, D.C. (p. 86).

Teachers will constantly need to make decisions about what to teach and how to teach it. Students, parents, and other teachers will also rely on scores to compare students or groups of students. This emphasizes the need for sound assessment practices. However, developing a portfolio for each concept learned is impractical. Likewise, relying on objective measures leads to a narrow view of what students can really do in science. Therefore, a combination of all available assessment procedures will provide data for objective decisions. Assessment is an ongoing process and should be integral with the curriculum.

Summary of the Assessment Standards.
The *NSES* provide emphasis on:

Assessing what is most highly valued.

Assessing rich, well-structured knowledge.

Assessing scientific understanding and reasoning.

Assessing to learn what students do understand.

Assessing achievement and opportunity to learn.

Students engaged in ongoing assessment of their work and that of others.

Teachers involved in the development of external assessments.

Reprinted with permission from the National Science Education Standards ©1996, National Academy of Sciences, courtesy of the National Academy Press, Washington, D.C. (p. 100).

In summary, assessment practices need to be changed to align them with the standards. Instead of the usual end-of the chapter multiple choice test provided with a text, assessment needs to be constant with how science is learned. They must also be fair, valid and reliable. Ongoing assessment through portfolios and authentic learning tasks will provide data that indicates whether the students are achieving the standards.

Linda's Assessment Strategy

Linda is now well into the school year and is enjoying teaching science through inquiry. Her students are progressing in their understanding of scientific concepts. She is at a grade-level meeting where the teachers are discussing their results with the standards-based science education program. Ann, one of the other fourth grade teachers, comments that she is not seeing very good results with the new way her class is doing science. After some discussion, it was determined that Ann was using the same tests that she had used for the past five years. Linda provides insight into what the problem is:

I began my transition into standards-based assessment in a similar way by trying to teach one way and testing another. As you are finding, it just does not work. Students in my class now do not even realize they are being assessed since it is just a normal part of every activity— writing a summary about the nature walk in their journal, creating a new animal based on what they found out about adaption, developing a poem which expresses the components of the environment, or writing and illustrating their own story for our classroom library. Since we are aligning the evaluation with the activities, the students really are showing me that they understand the concepts. I even have parent volunteers coming in this week to help with the books and listen to stories.

Linda is excited about her teaching because the students are so involved in what they are doing. Ann and some of the other teachers agree to try out authentic assessment.

Grade-level meeting
Results with the
standards-based science
education program.
Use Authentic
Assessment instead of
the same tests used for
the past five years.

Parent volunteers
Authentic Assessment

SCIENCE CONTENT STANDARDS

What Role Does Science Content Play in the Reform Effort?

The past sections have been primarily from the teacher's focal point and include how to teach and assess science. This section presents the National Science Education Content Standards, which are provided from the students' perspective. They represent what students should understand in the areas of physical, life, and earth and space science. They also establish the kinds of concepts and processes important for students' complete understanding of the science endeavor.

The Content Standards are somewhat different from what you would expect with traditional science textbooks or district curriculum guides. The *NSES,* in support of the reform efforts, contain fewer concepts. Instead of *breadth* of content with children studying numerous topics in minimal detail, the Content Standards provide *depth* of coverage on the most important topics. The topics were determined by the thousands of scientists, educators, and other experts.

Another way that the Content Standards are supportive of the reform effort is that they are designed to be achievement benchmarks for *all* students. At the end of each grade-level set, all students should know the major concepts and should be able to do the important processes which are stated in the Content Standards.

What Rationale Guided the Development of the Content Standards?

The *NSES* Content Standards are written with the nature of inquiry in mind. They do not mandate what to do in the classroom, rather, they are a set of reasonable outcomes of science education. The Content Standards are divided into levels K-4, 5-8, and 9-12. The eight categories of content standards are:

Unifying concepts and processes in science.

Science as inquiry.

Physical science.

Life science.

Earth and space science.

Science and technology.

Science in personal and social perspectives.

History and nature of science.

Reprinted with permission from the National Science Education Standards ©1996, National Academy of Sciences, courtesy of the National Academy Press, Washington, D.C. (p. 104).

Looking at the categories, you can see that the first one requires a unity of process and knowledge from kindergarten throughout twelfth grade. This is a *big picture* category, not only representing a unity of scientific processes and scientific content, but a marriage with other disciplines. It is the rationale for integrated or *whole learning*. Learning about science through children's literature, learning mathematics through science activities, or understanding the influence of scientific discoveries and their resulting technologies on society, are examples of unifying concepts.

The seven remaining categories are sequentially provided in a developmentally-appropriate manner. Science as inquiry is the first and most important category for the early years. The inquiry develops the foundation for physical science, which leads into life science and so on. Each category is developed as students progress through grades K-12. Unity also continues as students progress in school, allowing for a full understanding of the history and nature of science and what that means on a personal/ societal basis.

What are the Unifying Concepts and Processes?

There are some very important underlying constructs that are a part of the category described as *unifying concepts and processes in science.* These constructs are basic to understanding science and the applications of science to society. The *NSES* provides the following as examples:

Systems, order, and organization.

Evidence, models, and explanation.

Change, constancy, and measurement.

Evolution and equilibrium.

Form and function.

Reprinted with permission from the National Science Education Standards ©1996, National Academy of Sciences, courtesy of the National Academy Press, Washington, D.C. (p. 104).

Understanding systems and how they operate and interact, examining the consistent

change in nature, or working with models of abstract, sometimes non-observable phenomena are very complex understandings. It takes a systematic program of inquiry at each grade level to contribute to an overall understanding of what are called the *powerful ideas of science.* Correspondingly, the American Association for the Advancement of Science, in their own major science education reform effort titled *Project 2061: Science for All Americans* (1989) also list major science themes such as *Systems, Models, Consistency, Patterns of Change, Evolution,* and *Scale.* These common understandings are the backbone of what science is and how science is done. They are the center of inquiry in the classroom, in the scientist's lab, or in everyday life.

What is the Significance of Inquiry?

Past reform efforts such as the wave of new programs developed after the *Sputnik* crisis have focused on process skills needed to do science. The *NSES* also place a high priority on the processes of science but look to a bigger picture. What context do these processes fit into? The answer is scientific inquiry. We use the process skills to promote scientific understanding, satisfy the curiosity to know, engage in problem solving, develop critical thinking skills, and cultivate the relationships between science, technology and society. Engaging students in inquiry helps students develop lifelong skills to think through everyday situations and make responsible decisions for the future. Engaging students in inquiry helps students develop:

Understanding of scientific concepts.

An appreciation of "how we know" what we know in science.

Understanding of the nature of science.

Skills necessary to become independent inquirers about the natural world.

The dispositions to use the skills, abilities, and attitudes associated with science.

How is Inquiry Developed Throughout the Grade Levels?

Inquiry is so basic to science that every activity should support it in one way or another. There are two basic strands of inquiry which are developed at each of the three grade levels, K-4, 5-8 and 9-12.

Abilities necessary to do scientific inquiry.

Understanding about scientific inquiry.

The type of activities and depth of inquiry will change as students progress through school, but the outcomes of the use of inquiry will be the same. These outcomes include the students asking questions based on an activity, observation or new concept; the use of scientific skills to design and carry out an experiment to prove or disprove a hypothesis; the communication of the data and conclusions which they found through experimentation; the ability to use the scientific method and critical thinking to solve scientific and everyday problems; and the ability to understand scientific research, to support their opinions through research or investigation, and to know when a study is flawed or not scientifically based.

Developmentally, students will become increasingly more competent in inquiry if it is supported at every grade level. Often times, teachers will express that their students need to know certain vocabulary words, or facts about science in order for the next year's science curriculum. Vocabulary will come naturally, however, as it is used in daily inquiry. Teachers do not have to *drill and kill* vocabulary and definitions that students learn sooner or later, as naturally as a child first learns to speak the words which are meaningful to them. Inquiry, on the other hand, is something which is important to build upon each school day of each year. Chaille and Britain (1997) discuss how the young child should be viewed as a *scientist* in the classroom. This attitude will promote scientific inquiry and skill development.

Scientific skill development cannot be learned in a short period of time. Many science methods professors will attest to this when trying to make up for years of lost inquiry in one or two college courses. It is not often a challenge for college students to memorize vocabulary and definitions for a multiple choice test. It can be much more difficult for a college student to design and conduct an experiment or problem solve.

What Indicates if a Content Standard is Important?

As you begin to use the content standards, you may ask yourself how a particular standard was developed. With so many scientists and others involved, how could they ever agree? The answer is in the fundamental ideas associated with the Content Standards. A Content Standard is fundamental if it:

Represents a central event or phenomenon in the natural world.

Represents a central scientific idea and organizing principle.

Has rich explanatory power.

Guides fruitful investigations.

Applies to situations and contexts common to everyday experiences.

Can be linked to meaningful learning experiences.

Is developmentally appropriate for students at the grade level specified.

What Guidelines Should My School Have for Using the Standards?

Not every school will use the *NSES* to the same degree. Some States have developed their own sets of science standards. Generally there is a lot of overlap between the state standards and the *NSES,* just as there is over 90 percent correlation between the *NSES* and the American Association for the Advancement of Science *Benchmarks for Scientific Literacy* (1993.) In general, the following guidelines should be used relative to the *NSES.*

None of the eight categories of content standards should be eliminated. For instance, students should have opportunities to learn science in personal and social perspectives and to learn about the history and nature of science, as well as to learn subject matter, in the school science program.

No standards should be eliminated from a category. For instance, "biological evolution" cannot be eliminated from the life science standards.

Science content can be added. The connections, depth, detail, and selection of topics can be enriched and varied as appropriate for individual students and school science programs. However, addition of content must not prevent the learning of fundamental concepts by all students.

The content standards must be used in the context of the standards on teaching and assessment. Using the standards with traditional teaching

and assessment strategies defeats the intentions of the National Science Education Standards.

How Do the Content Standards Differ From Existing Curricula?

The Content Standards represent a new focus on how to teach (through inquiry) and what to teach (less content but in more depth). They emphasize:

Understanding scientific concepts and developing abilities of inquiry;

Learning subject matter disciplines in the context of inquiry, technology, science in personal and social perspectives, and history and nature of science;

Integrating all aspects of science content;

Studying a few fundamental science concepts;

Implementing inquiry as instructional strategies, abilities, and ideas to be learned.

Inquiry is further promoted with the emphasis on:

Activities that investigate and analyze science questions.

Investigations over extended periods of time.

Process skills in context.

Using multiple process skills--manipulation, cognitive, procedural.

Using evidence and strategies for developing or revising an explanation

Sampler of National Science Education Standards

Science as argument and explanation.

Communicating science explanations.

Groups of students often analyzing and synthesizing data after defending conclusions.

Doing more investigations in order to develop understanding, ability, values of inquiry and knowledge of science content.

Applying the results of experiments to scientific arguments and explanations.

Management of ideas and information.

Public communication of student ideas and work to classmates.

Reprinted with permission from the National Science Education Standards ©1996, National Academy of Sciences, courtesy of the National Academy Press, Washington, D.C. (p. 113).

Summary

The best way to approach content standards implementation is to bring together the teachers, administration, and parents and ask some important questions. Many people agree that standards are relevant, but not everyone can agree on what standards are important. In other words, who's set of standards should be used (e.g. *NSES,* AAAS *Benchmarks,* state standards, standards developed by business groups or religious groups)? Keep in mind that there were thousands of professionals who provided input into the *NSES.* They have been refined to include the most important things for K-12 students. Next, the question becomes how to implement the standards. Discuss who will check assessments, what benchmarks will be in place to see if there is progress toward achieving the standards. Finally, ask how will the standards differ from our existing curricula.

The *NSES* document provides a guide to each of the content standards. The guide is an expansion and explanation of the standards.

Linda's Use of Content Standards

Linda was hesitant to begin using the *NSES* before she attended the *NSTA* convention. This is because she was confused as to why the *NSES* were any better than the curriculum which the district had planned during the summer inservice seven years ago. She knew of other teachers who had helped establish the curriculum document and they seemed to be very professional. One conversation that Linda had at the convention made her realize why the district's curriculum was problematic. She found out that most of the American school district curriculums contain too many topics for any one to be covered in the detail sufficient for inquiry. It became clear to Linda that she would have to look for the most critical topics in the *NSES.*

Most of the American school district curriculums contain too many topics for any one to be covered in the detail sufficient for inquiry. I'll have to look for the most critical topics in the NSES.

THE PHYSICAL SCIENCE STANDARDS

Levels K-4
Properties of objects and materials

Position and motion of objects

Light, heat, electricity, and magnetism

Levels 5-8
Properties and changes of properties in matter

Motions and forces

Transfer of energy

Levels 9-12
Structure of atoms

Structure and properties of matter

Chemical reactions

Motions and forces

Conservation of energy and increase in disorder

Interactions of energy and matter

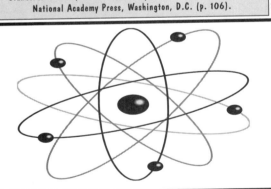

Physical Science in Linda's Classroom

Linda really enjoys teaching a unit on water. It makes learning about the properties of objects and materials interesting. The students are captivated when Linda makes a large bubble around each of them to show how the property of water can change when things are added to it such as dish soap and glycerine. Students also learn through an activity where Linda provides them with beakers, stoppers, ice, a hotplate, and safety materials and challenges them to make a cloud. The students discover the phases of water and how temperature changes affect water. Later they integrate geography and math into the lessons by determining how much of the Earth is covered with water. Linda conducts an activity where students throw an inflatable globe to each other and where the right index finger touches, the student describes whether the part on that spot is water or land. Then they must name the country or body of water.

Another challenging activity is to determine the level of water near the school if the Earth were to retain more heat and melt the Polar ice caps. There were a lot of good predictions and students discovered, through a modeling activity and a discussion of global warming, the importance of the interaction between science, technology, and society. They integrated language arts and art into this activity by developing a short story and picture of what they predicted would happen if the Earth retained more heat.

Life Science in Linda's Classroom

Linda is excited to begin her investigation of life science this year. As part of her professional development this past summer, she participated in a Project WILD (1992) workshop. Linda is eager to use the Oh Deer! and Habitat Lap Sit activities. These activities help teach the concept that food, water, shelter, and space are important to living things. She also sought support from a small grant from a local industry's foundation and was funded to develop a butterfly garden (Grambo, 1995) and an aquarium. Now, the children will study firsthand the life cycles and environments of some animals. Music will also be integrated into this unit when students develop songs about nature and conservation.

Another unit Linda is planning is based on Project Learning Tree (1994). She wants the students to discover through the Tree Factory and Tree Cookie activities that the tree has a particular structure and the importance of not harming the tree as it grows. Linda also plans to invite a forester from the local paper company and a state forest ranger to help out with other activities. She wants to stress, through forestry practices, the interaction of women and men and his and her environment. Linda also finds that this type of activity is a good way to provide career information.

EARTH AND SPACE SCIENCE STANDARDS

Levels K-4
Properties of earth material
Objects in the sky
Changes in earth and sky

Levels 5-8
Structure of the earth system
Earth's history
Earth in the solar system

Levels 9-12
Energy in the earth system
Geochemical cycles
Origin and evolution of the earth system
Origin and evolution of the universe

Reprinted with permission from the National Science Education Standards ©1996, National Academy of Sciences, courtesy of the National Academy Press, Washington, D.C. (p. 107).

Earth and Space Science in Linda's Classroom

Linda wondered how to get started with earth and space science. She had always involved her students with a unit on weather but this particular unit was not inquiry-based.

Linda remembered a recent book titled *Resources for teaching elementary school science* (National Academy of Sciences, 1996). Looking through this guide, she found an entire section dedicated to earth science containing a variety of curriculum materials. To her surprise, there was even a section on places nearby to visit. National activities such as *Project Atmosphere* from the American Meteorological Society were referenced there as well. It did not take Linda long to gather resources and begin the planning. Her students will even help out later by writing letters and seeking materials to use in their own projects.

Later in the year, Linda will initiate an Internet-based unit on the planets. She will begin a *KWL* unit with listing everything the students *Know* about the planets. Then the class will list what they *Want* to know and set out surfing the Internet in search of answers and more questions. Last year, Linda's class visited *NASA*'s site, searched many resources from universities and wrote electronic letters to astronomers listed on the Internet. Later, as the group got back together for the *What was Learned* discussions, many new questions and interesting answers about the planets were discussed. The students integrated math by completing activities such as how old they would be when they arrived at each of the planets if they were to take the space shuttle. Her students this year will be excited about generating so many of their own interesting questions as well as being equally surprised at the answers.

Science and Technology in Linda's Classroom

Linda was sure that this year she would address the Science and Technology Standards. The grade level teachers were planning a technology invention convention. Students will determine a need for an invention, design a nonworking model of a possible invention, and share with the classmates what scientific principles or discoveries contributed to the development of their project.

Linda was initially inspired to work on inventions by an article called "Rube Goldberg Contraptions" in Science Scope (Cox, 1994). Now she is contacting the National Science Teachers Association's web page (http://www.nsta.org/) to find out about current science and technology fairs in her area.

Parents will again be invited to the invention convention to provide support for their child's learning. Last year there were many interesting things such as a global positioning instrument for a bicycle so parents could tell where their children were riding and a computer-based device which sampled television shows and determined if they were educational, suggestive, or violent.

SCIENCE IN PERSONAL AND SOCIAL PERSPECTIVES STANDARDS

Levels K-4
Personal health
Characteristics and changes in populations
Types of resources
Changes in environments
Science and technology in local challenges

Levels 5-8
Personal health
Populations, resources, and environments
Natural hazards
Risks and benefits
Science and technology in society

Levels 9-12
Personal and community health
Population growth
Natural resources
Environmental quality
Natural and human-induced hazards
Science and technology in local, national, and global challenges

Reprinted with permission from the National Science Education Standards ©1996, National Academy of Sciences, courtesy of the National Academy Press, Washington, D.C. (p. 108).

Science in Personal and Social Perspectives in Linda's Classroom

Linda plans to provide some fictitious scenarios for students to debate again this year. As part of the study of government this year, students will take on the role of a variety of elected and appointed officials, debating the issues and seeking support for legislation dealing with the issues. They will be provided with a limited budget to fund studies related to the issues or hire additional personnel to manage or work on aspects of the scenario related to how the current government operates.

One scenario used last year was that the town had record unemployment with fishing as the primary source of income. An oil company was considering relocating to the area and drilling offshore for what was determined to be a very large quality of oil. This would create numerous high-paying jobs which would, in turn, support other jobs in the community. The danger was in the potential harm to the environment and fishing industry.

History and Nature of Science in Linda's Classroom

Linda wants to take the opportunity proposed in this standard to work on science as a human endeavor for both males and females. She did an activity last year where students described a scientist and what the scientist does. The results were very disheartening. The contrived scientists were all older men with wild hair wearing a lab coat. They worked day and night in a dark and musty laboratory, never to see their family.

Since Linda's town is near a major research and industrial center where jobs for scientists are generally available, she wanted to promote the fact that both boys and girls can choose a career in science. She also wants to stress that culture or ethnic background should not prevent someone from a career as a scientist. Gender and cultural diversity should not matter since there are many areas of science that are fun and interesting. Linda plans on inviting many female scientists into her classroom since not one female came to mind as Linda asked the students to name a scientist.

Assessment policies and practices should be aligned with the goals, student expectations, and curriculum frameworks.

Support systems and formal and informal expectations of teachers must be aligned with the goals, student expectations and curriculum frameworks.

Responsibility needs to be clearly defined for determining, supporting, maintaining, and upgrading all elements of the science program.

SCIENCE PROGRAM STANDARDS

Curriculum, instruction, and learning should be envisioned school- and district-wide, kindergarten through 12th grade, rather than as a set of lessons taught by a single teacher during a preset time period. As the following standards will indicate, this enables teams of teachers to be in charge of their own curriculum. The administration becomes a support partner rather than curriculum director.

Program Standard A–Program Consistency.

All elements of the K-12 science program must be consistent with the other National Science Education Standards and with one another and developed within and across grade levels to meet a clearly stated set of goals.

In an effective science program, a set of clear goals and expectations for students must be used to guide the design, implementation, and assessment of all elements of the science program.

Curriculum frameworks should be used to guide the selection and development of units and courses of study.

Teaching practices need to be consistent with the goals and curriculum frameworks.

Science education for some schools has been a haphazard approach of each teacher interpreting a vague curriculum guide. In other schools, teachers followed a curriculum guide which was filled with so many new concepts, little time was left for things like inquiry or authentic assessment. Still in other schools, science education was not a part of the curriculum at all but left up to the individual teacher's discretion. What the standards call for is a clearly articulated set of expectations, strategies for implementation, and a related assessment scheme.

Program Standard B–Appropriate, Integrated, and Interesting.

The program of study in science for all students should be developmentally appropriate, interesting, and relevant to students' lives; emphasizing student understanding through inquiry; and connected with other school subjects.

The program of study should include all of the content standards.

Science content must be embedded in a variety of curriculum patterns that are developmentally appropriate, interesting, and relevant to students' lives.

The program of study must emphasize student understanding through inquiry.

The program of study in science should connect to other school subjects.

Children often come to school as natural scientists–eager to explore. Often times, a poorly designed program steals this natural curiosity away. Science becomes like a foreign language for students. It is a language students attempt to translate into a meaningful story. They soon find that there is something missing in the translation, however. This is because even a foreign language text also includes stories which are a part of the culture. Since the *culture* of science is inquiry, then how could the *science story* possibly make sense. It would have to be made relevant to the students, taught at their developmental level, and done with inquiry as the basis. It would have to be connected to their everyday life and to other subjects whenever possible.

Program Standard C–Mathematics Integration.

The science program should be coordinated with the mathematics program to enhance student use and understanding of mathematics in the study of science and to improve student understanding of mathematics.

Many of the changes suggested in the science standards are also changes which are a part of the National Council of Teachers of Mathematics *Curriculum and Evaluation Standards for School Mathematics.* (1989). Both sets of standards call for integration between mathematics and science because neither one can be done effectively in isolation.

Program Standard D–Equipment and Resources.

The K-12 science program must give students access to appropriate and sufficient resources, including quality teachers, time, materials and equipment, adequate and safe space, and the community.

The most important resource is professional teachers.

Time is a major resource in a science program.

Conducting scientific inquiry requires that students have easy, equitable, and frequent opportunities to use a wide range of equipment, materials, supplies, and other resources for experimentation and direct investigation of phenomena.

Collaborative inquiry requires adequate and safe space.

Good science programs require access to the world beyond the classroom.

Teachers often ask what they can do to change the equipment and resource condition at their school. This standard suggests that the teachers themselves are the most important resource. This is certainly true since the teacher is the one who can place more time and emphasis on inquiry, seek parent and community support for their classroom science program, and plan for guest speakers and field trips. Fortunately, time spent on science is increasing according to national studies (Division of Research, Evaluation, and Communication, Directorate for Education and Human Resources, 1996). Teachers are placing an increased emphasis on science which is most likely in response to current reform efforts and standards-based initiatives.

Program Standard E–Opportunity.

All students in the K-12 science program must have equitable access to opportunities to achieve the National Science Education Standards.

This standard is concerned with equity across cultures, gender, and physical or mental disabilities. In sum, each student should have every opportunity to achieve excellence in science education. Teaching, with this perspective in mind, requires constant connections between science and the everyday world of the students.

Program Standard F–Community and Support.

Schools must work as communities that encourage, support, and sustain teachers as they implement an effective science program.

Schools must explicitly support reform efforts in an atmosphere of openness and trust that encourages collegiality.

Regular time needs to be provided and teachers encouraged to discuss, reflect, and conduct research around science education reform.

Teachers must be supported in creating and being members of networks of reform.

An effective leadership structure that includes teachers must be in place.

Individual teachers who adhere to the standards in isolation from other teachers may soon find that they are overwhelmed. Time management issues, lack of support, and administration or community opposition to science education reform proposed by the standards may make it difficult to be an effective change agent in the classroom. Schools must be communities of support and encouragement in order for teachers to carry out the vision of the *NSES*.

Summary of the Program Standards.

The *NSES* Program Standards are supportive of system-wide change. They place emphasis on:

Coordinating the development of the K-12 science program across grade levels.

Aligning curriculum, teaching, and assessment.

Allocating resources necessary for hands-on inquiry teaching aligned with the Standards.

Curriculum that supports the Standards, and includes a variety of components, such as laboratories emphasizing inquiry and field trips.

Curriculum that includes natural phenomena and science-related social issues that students encounter in everyday life.

Connecting science to other school subjects, such as mathematics and social studies.

Providing challenging opportunities for all students to learn science.

Involving successful teachers of science in the hiring process.

Treating teachers as professionals whose work requires opportunities for continual learning and networking.

Promoting collegiality among teachers as a team to improve the school.

Teachers as decision-makers.

Reprinted with permission from the National Science Education Standards ©1996, National Academy of Sciences, courtesy of the National Academy Press, Washington, D.C. (p. 224).

A good science education program at any level will be a amalgamation of a relevant, inquiry-based curriculum, teachers willing to work toward achieving high standards, a community of learners where everyone has an opportunity to learn, and administration and community support to make sure that the program can be achieved. The Program Standards summarize how to make this vision possible.

Linda's School-Wide Effect

As Linda grew more confident in her teaching science through inquiry, she could not wait to share her experiences with the other teachers at her school. Many of them tried various activities and some teachers began to ask how the entire school could implement a program based on the standards. These teachers investigated this possibility and found that between the science, social studies, mathematics, and other standards, they could develop an integrated standards-based program at their school. They began to plan for the next year. Each teacher would be responsible for an integrated topic of their choice. This unit would include all of the subject areas and address related standards. It took several after-school meetings, but the teachers enjoyed showcasing their unit plans and seeking the expertise of others in refining them to include all of the necessary content and skills.

One sample unit on energy included science (energy production, transmission, and distribution), social studies (the effect of increased energy use on America's workforce and use of resources), reading (children's literature stories on energy topics), language arts (writing poetry describing a night without energy), mathematics (calculating the use of electricity and estimating future use), art (the use of electronic paintbrushes versus artist's brushes), music (electronic versus wooden and metal instruments), and physical education (energy use for health). The unit also included the scientific skills of observation, classification, inference, measurement, prediction, identifying variables, describing relationships between variables, constructing hypotheses, designing investigations, experimentation, and communication. Soon other groups of teachers became interested and programmatic changes began to occur at their school.

Linda even has the parents involved. She read "Bringing Families and Science Together" (Gardner, 1996) in the Science and Children theme issue on families (1996). It reemphasized the importance of the family as part of the science program.

SCIENCE EDUCATION SYSTEM STANDARDS

One reason for the change away from an administrative-directed to a teacher-directed science education program is to promote teacher ownership of the science education program. Teachers participating in meaningful inquiry-based inservice, selecting textbooks which support student learning through hands-on/minds on activities, using relevant assessment techniques, and designing *NSES*-based classroom curriculum and activities can, and will, support each other's efforts. There exists a consistency across units instead of school boards, senior-level district supervisors, and even union leaders attempting to put their conflicting or fragmented visions into the classrooms.

System Standard A–Congruency.

Policies that influence the practice of science education must be congruent with the program, teaching, professional development, assessment, and content standards while allowing for adaptation to local circumstances.

Reprinted with permission from the National Science Education Standards ©1996, National Academy of Sciences, courtesy of the National Academy Press, Washington, D.C. (p. 230).

This standard speaks to the policy-makers at the district level or above. It is an important standard for teachers as well. It challenges teachers to become involved in determining policy. Teachers should maintain communication with legislators, seek positions on policy-development committees, and similar activities. Choice schools are becoming popular. Often times, teachers have a lot of input into what choice of curriculum their school will offer. When this occurs, teachers should revisit the *NSES* to be sure that their school will support needed changes in science education.

System Standard B–Coordination.

Policies that influence science education should be coordinated within and across agencies, institutions, and organizations.

Reprinted with permission from the National Science Education Standards ©1996, National Academy of Sciences, courtesy of the National Academy Press, Washington, D.C. (p. 231).

Coordination across units is essential for any reform effort to take place. What is not self-evident is that teachers should be involved in the coordination activity since there will be policy makers who do not understand the science content or skills involved in the polices.

System Standard C–Long-Term Effort.

Policies need to be sustained over sufficient time to provide the continuity necessary to bring about the changes required by the Standards.

Reprinted with permission from the National Science Education Standards ©1996, National Academy of Sciences, courtesy of the National Academy Press, Washington, D.C. (p. 231).

History shows that previous science education reform efforts looked for immediate results. The reason why there is such a need for the *NSES* today is that we know this did not work in the past. Ongoing, systematic reform is needed.

System Standard D–Support.

Policies must be supported with resources.

Reprinted with permission from the National Science Education Standards ©1996, National Academy of Sciences, courtesy of the National Academy Press, Washington, D.C. (p. 232).

Resource management is an important issue facing school boards, state education agencies, and the federal government. The vision of the standards cannot be achieved in full without adequate support. From a teacher's standpoint, it is important to provide information as to how past support has made a difference and how future support will be used. It is also beneficial to seek community support or grant support for science education programs.

System Standard E–Equality.
Science education policies must be equitable.

This standard should be self-evident. Yet the pathway to its achievement may take creative efforts of teachers and policy makers if this standard is to be achieved. Ideas such as collaborative, Internet-based science education projects, model science/technology schools of choice, and distance education courses will certainly help achieve the goal of equity in science education.

System Standard F–Review.
All policy instruments must be reviewed for possible unintended effects on the classroom practice of science education.

Review, at the classroom, school, district, state, federal, and even international level is essential to monitor the effectiveness of the *NSES*. Assessment data from all levels needs rigorous analysis to look for successes as well as unintended effects of *NSES* implementation.

System Standard G–New Visions.
Responsible individuals must take the opportunity afforded by the standards-based reform movement to achieve the new vision of science education portrayed in the Standards.

From the very first standard to the last, the role of teachers cannot be overemphasized. Teachers are the key to reform and the role of the teacher is changing to one where they facilitate student learning rather than dispense knowledge (Sivertsen, 1993).

Summary of the System Standards.
The *NSES* speak to district, state, and federal systems. At the district level, they emphasize:

Ongoing professional development to support teachers.

Policies designed to support changes called for in the Standards.

Purchase or adoption of curriculum aligned with the Standards and on a conceptual approach to science teaching, including support for hands-on science materials.

Assessments aligned with the Standards.

Teacher leadership in improvement of science education.

Authority for decisions at level of implementation.

School board support of improvements aligned with the Standards.

Local union contracts that support improvements indicated by the Standards.

Every group involved in the education of our K-12 students must work together in the coming years and share a common vision provided by the Standards for true reform to occur. It is important that each group work to better understand the roles and responsibilities of the others and be supportive of the reform effort.

Results of Linda's Efforts

Linda had a far reaching effect on her school. She is an example of a teacher becoming involved with inquiry, and working to promote its use in the classroom. It may be a long time before such efforts become part of a system-wide change in her district. There will always be some resistance to change. Likewise, there will be teachers, administrators, school boards, education leaders or business partners who do not understand the significance of the vision of the NSES. This is acknowledged by the National Research Council and the American Association for the Advancement of Science by their statements of a "long-term effort". AAAS has set its sights on the year 2061 for all Americans to be scientifically literate (since their project began with the arrival of Halley's comet and will be completed with the return of the comet.) Your help as a teacher will realize AAAS' goal and the NSES vision.

Vision of the NSES.

National Research Council
and
American Association for
the Advancement of Science
"long-term effort".

AAAS—by the year 2061
all Americans will be
scientifically literate.

Your help as a teacher will
realize AAAS' goal and the
NSES' vision.

CONCLUSIONS AND FURTHER RESOURCES

The Challenge Provided in the *NSES*.
If I Want to Learn More, Where Do I Go From Here?

CONCLUSIONS AND FURTHER RESOURCES

The Challenge Provided in the *NSES*.

The *NSES* document ends with a challenge for those involved in science education. They encourage:

Students to use the Standards to set personal learning goals and experience the satisfaction of understanding the natural world;

Teachers of science to use the Standards as the basis for improving science content, teaching, and assessment;

Science supervisors to use the Standards to implement new, long-range plans for improving science education at the state and local levels;

Science educators to change programs in colleges and universities and develop exemplary materials based on the Standards;

School administrators to focus attention on the need for materials, equipment, and staff development aligned with the Standards;

Those who work in museums, zoos, and science centers to use the Standards as an opportunity to collaborate in providing rich science learning experiences for students;

Parents and community members to use the Standards to contribute to their children's science education and generate support for higher-quality school science programs;

Scientists and engineers to use the Standards to work with school personnel to initiate and sustain the improvement of school science programs;

Business and industry to use the Standards to help schools and science teachers with guidance and resources for developing high-quality programs; and

Legislators and public officials to strive for policies and funding priorities aligned with the National Science Education Standards.

Reprinted with permission from the National Science Education Standards ©1996, National Academy of Sciences, courtesy of the National Academy Press, Washington, D.C. (p. 244-245).

These challenges are achievable if everyone, especially you, help out. Your reading of this sampler is a good start. Keep in mind that the sampler was not written to replace the *NSES*. Rather, it is provided to cause you to want to explore the *NSES* in more detail. I would hope, if you haven't already done so, that you use the order form at the beginning of this sampler to purchase the original document. It is filled with easy-to-read explanations and examples of what the educational, scientific, and policy-making community envisioned are necessary to make the *NSES* a reality. There are numerous vignettes to place the principles of the *NSES* into a meaningful context. Once you see the big picture of the meaning of the NSES, you will begin to realize that standards-based reform is important to your students' future. I believe that you will discover the many opportunities to use the information in your own classroom. Inquiry is really interesting and fun for students at every grade level and throughout life.

If I Want to Learn More, Where Do I Go From Here?

There are a few ways to proceed from here. First, try out some inquiry activities in your classroom or practicum site, if you have not already done this. It will open the door to a new world of learning. A door which is hard to close because the students will be eager to learn more.

A second way to proceed is to find out who is responsible for the curriculum in your school or district. Generally, districts employ science supervisors. The supervisors are the ones who arrange for inservice opportunities and are primarily responsible for the curriculum and assessment in the sciences. Ask the supervisor what opportunities are available for you to expand your knowledge of the standards, inquiry methods, and scientific content. Also ask them who to contact for help or funding opportunities for such things like equipment, Internet connections, guest speakers for your classroom, substitutes while you participate in science conferences, or available distance learning courses. You may also talk with your principal to see who can assist you with inservice and materials at the school.

It is never too early to consider professional development opportunities. As you begin your next school year, try to contact your grade level science specialist, the school's curriculum coordinator, a community scientist, a business representative, or a local college science educator to see what the possibilities are for incorporating the vision of the standards into your classroom. You may even want to consider an action research project based on the *NSES*. In any event, you will find that the rewards seen with your students will make it all worthwhile.

Another way to proceed is to look at further printed and electronic resources. There are numerous documents available to you, many of which are available through the Internet. The following section lists references and resources for further reading.

Try out some inquiry activities in your classroom or practicum site.

Find out who is responsible for the curriculum in your school or district

Consider professional development opportunities

Look at further printed and electronic resources.

REFERENCES AND RESOURCES

References Used in This Sampler.

American Association for the Advancement of Science. (1989). *Project 2061: Science for all Americans.* Washington, DC: Author.

American Association for the Advancement of Science. (1993). *Benchmarks for scientific literacy.* New York: Oxford University Press.

American Forest Foundation. (1994). *Project learning tree.* Washington, DC: Author.

Chaille, C., & Britain, L. (1997). *The young child as scientist: A constructivist approach to early childhood education* (2nd. ed.). New York: Longman.

Council for Environmental Education. (1992). *Project WILD K-12 activity guide.* USA: Author.

Cox, J. (1994, January). Rube Goldberg contraptions. *Science Scope, 17* (4), 44-47.

Division of Research, Evaluation, and Communication, Directorate for Education and Human Resources. (1996). *The learning curve: What we are discovering about U.S. science and mathematics education.* L. E. Suter (Ed.). (NSF 96-53). Washington, DC: National Science Foundation.

Families involved in real science together (Theme issue). (1996, October). *Science and Children, 31,* (2).

Gardner, D. H. (1996, October). Bringing families and science together. *Science and Children, 34* (2), 14-16.

Grambo, G. (1995, May). Raising butterflies in your classroom. *Science Scope, 18* (8), 16-18.

Jones, R. M. (1990). *Teaming up!* LaPorte, TX: ITGROUP.

Linn, M. C., & Burbules, N. C. (1993). Construction of knowledge and group learning. In K. G. Tobin (Ed.). *The practice of constructivism in science education* (pp. 91-119). Washington DC: AAAS Press.

Marshall, S. P. (1997). Creating sustainable learning communities for the Twenty-First Century. In F. Hesselbein, M. Goldsmith, & R. Beckhard (Eds.). *The organization of the future* (pp. 177-188). San Francisco: Jossey-Bass Publishers.

National Academy of Sciences. (1996). *Resources for teaching elementary school science.* Washington, DC: National Academy Press.

National Academy of Sciences. (1997). *Science for all children. A guide for improving elementary science education in your school district.* Washington, DC: National Academy Press.

National Council of Teachers of Mathematics. (1989). *Curriculum and evaluation standards for school mathematics.* Reston, VA: Author.

National Science Teachers Association. (1996). *NSTA pathways to the science standards; Secondary school edition.* Arlington, VA: Author.

National Science Teachers Association. (1997). *NSTA pathways to the science standards; Elementary school edition.* Arlington, VA: Author.

Novak, J. D., & Gowin, B. (1984). *Learning how to learn.* Cambridge: Cambridge University Press.

Shulman, L. S. (1986). Those who understand: Knowledge growth in teaching. *Educational Researcher, 15* (2), 4-14.

Shulman, L. S. (1987). Knowledge and teaching foundations of the new reform. *Harvard Education Review, 57* (1), 1-22.

Sivertsen, M. L. (1993). *State of the art. Transforming ideas for teaching and learning science.* Washington, DC: U.S. Department of Education, Office of Research.

von Glasersfeld, E. (1989). Cognition, construction of knowledge, and teaching. *Synthese, 80,* 121-140.

Vygotsky, L. (1962). *Thought and language.* E. Hanfmann & G. Vakar (Eds.). Cambridge, MA: MIT Press.

Printed Resources for Further Investigation.

American Association for the Advancement of Science. (1998). *Blueprints for reform.* New York: Oxford University Press.

American Association for the Advancement of Science. (2001). *Atlas of science literacy.* New York: Oxford University Press.

American Association for the Advancement of Science. (2001). *Designs for science literacy.* New York: Oxford University Press.

Atkin, J. M., Black, P., & Coffey, J. (2001). *Classroom assessment and the national science education standards: A guide for teaching and learning.* Washington, DC: National Academy Press.

Bowers, P. S., & TeBockhorst, D. (1993). Science labs in the elementary school: One approach for improved concept and process skills attainment. In G. M. Madrazo Jr. & L. L. Motz (Eds.), *Sourcebook for science supervisors* (4th ed., pp. 109—112). Arlington, VA: National Science Teachers Association.

Brandwein, P. F., & Passow, H. A. (Eds.). (1989). *Gifted young in science.* Washington, DC: National Science Teachers Association.

BSCS. (1996). *National standards & the science curriculum. Challenges, opportunities, & recommendations.* Dubuque, IA: Kendall/Hunt Publishing Company.

Bybee, R. W. (1997). *Achieving scientific literacy: From purposes to practices.* Portsmouth, NH: Heinemann.

Carey, S. J. (Ed.). (1993) *Science for all cultures.* Arlington, VA: National Science Teachers Association.

Center for Science, Mathematics, and Engineering Education Staff. (1997). *Every child a scientist: Achieving scientific literacy for all.* Washington, DC: National Academy Press.

Center for Science, Mathematics, and Engineering Education Staff. (1997). *Improving student learning in mathematics and science: The role of national standards in state policy.* Washington, DC: National Academy Press.

Center for Science, Mathematics, and Engineering Education Staff. (1997). *Introducing the national science education standards, booklet.* Washington, DC: National Academy Press.

Coming up standards: What students should know and be able to do across disciplines (Special Report). (1995). *Education Week, 14* (29), 52-70.

Committee on Development of an Addendum to the National Science Education Standards on Science and Technology. (2000). *Science and technology and the national science education standards: A guide for teaching and learning.* Washington, DC: National Academy Press.

Committee on Developments in the Science of Learning. (2000). *How people learn: Brain, mind, experience, and school* (expanded ed.). Washington, DC: National Academy Press.

Committee on Science Education K-12 and the Mathematical Sciences Education Board, National Research Council. (1999). *Designing mathematics or science curriculum programs: A guide for using mathematics and science education standards.* Washington, DC: National Academy Press.

Committee on Understanding the Influence of Standards in Science, Mathematics, and Technology Education, Weiss, I. R., Hollweg, K. S., & Burrill, G. (Eds). (2001). *Considering the influence: A framework for research on the effects of nationally developed mathematics, science, and technology education standards.* Washington, DC: National Academy Press.

Davis, S., & Botkin, J. (1994). *The monster under the bed.* New York: Simon & Schuster.

Division of Elementary, Secondary, and Informal Education, Directorate for Education and Human Resources. (1997). *The challenge and promise of K-8 science education reform* (Foundations Monograph, Vol.1). Washington, DC: National Science Foundation.

Sampler of National Science Education Standards

Eby, J. W. (1992). *Reflective planning, teaching, and evaluation for the elementary school.* New York: Merrill.

Goodlad, J. I. (1994). *Educational renewal: Better teachers, better schools.* San Francisco: Jossey-Bass.

Johnson, D. W., & Johnson, R. T. (1994). *Learning together and alone: Cooperative, competitive and individualistic learning* (4th ed.). Boston: Allyn & Bacon.

Kulm, G., & Malcom, S. M. (Eds.). (1991). *Science assessment in the service of reform.* Washington, DC: American Association for the Advancement of Science.

Loucks-Horsley, S., Carlson, M. O., Brink, L. H., Horwitz, P., Marsh, D. P., Pratt, H., Roy, K. R., & Worth. K. (1989). *Developing and supporting teachers for elementary school science education.* Andover, MA: The National Center for Improving Science Education.

National Council of Teachers of Mathematics. (1991). *Professional standards for teaching mathematics.* Reston, VA: Author.

National Research Council. (1996). *The role of scientists in the professional development of science teachers.* Washington, DC: National Academy Press.

National Research Council Committee on Undergraduate Science Education. (1997). *Science teaching reconsidered: A handbook.* Washington, DC: National Academy Press.

Olson, S., & Loucks-Horsley, S. (Eds.). (2000). *Inquiry and the national science education standards: A guide for teaching and learning.* Washington, DC: National Academy Press.

Ostlund, K., & Mercier, S. (1996). *Rising to the challange of the national science education standards. The process of science inquiry.* Fresno, CA: S & K Associates.

Paulu, N., & Martin, M. (1991). *Helping your child learn science.* Washington, DC: U.S. Department of Education, Office of Educational Research and Improvement.

Pearce, C. R. (1999). *Nurturing inquiry: Real science for the elementary classroom.* Portsmouth, NH: Heinemann.

Raizen, S. A., Baron, J. B., Champagne, A. B., Haertel, E., Mullis, I. V. S., & Oakes, J. (1989). *Assessment in elementary school science education.* Washington, DC: The NETWORK and Biological Sciences Curriculum Study.

Rhoton, J., & Bowers, P. (1996). *Issues in science education.* Arlington, VA: National Science Teachers Association.

Rhoton, J., & Bowers, P. (2001). *Professional development leadership and the diverse learner.* Arlington, VA: National Science Teachers Association.

Rhoton, J., & Bowers, P. (2001). *Professional development planning and design.* Arlington, VA: National Science Teachers Association.

Siebert, E. D., & McIntosh, W. J. (2001). *College pathways to the science education standards.* Arlington, VA: National Science Teachers Association.

Singer, M., & Tuomi, J. (Eds.). (1999). *Selecting instructional materials: A guide for K-12 science.* Washington, DC: National Academy Press.

Sussman, A. (Ed.). (1993). *Science education partnerships: Manual for scientists and K-12 teachers.* San Francisco, CA: University of California Press.

Tobin, K. (Ed.). (1993). *The practice of constructivism in science education.* Washington, DC: AAAS Press.

Wellman, R. T. (1978). Science: A basic for language development. In M. B. Rowe (Ed.), *What research says to the science teacher* (Vol. 1). Washington, DC: National Science Teachers Association.

Working Group on Teaching Evolution, National Academy of Sciences. (1998). *Teaching about evolution and the nature of science.* Washington, DC: National Academy Press.

Yager, R. (1991). The constructivist learning model. *The Science Teacher, 58*(6), 52-57.

Yager, R. E. (Ed.). (1993). *The science, technology, society movement. What research says to the science teacher* (Vol. 7). Arlington, VA: National Science Teachers Association.

Sample Science Education Web Sites.

Access Excellence Activities Exchange
http://www.accessexcellence.org/AE/

Amazing Space
http://amazing-space.stsci.edu/

American Association for the Advancement of
Science
http://www.aaas.org/

American Association for the Advancement of
Science Project 2061
http://www.project2061.org/

American Association of Physics Teachers
http://www.aapt.org/

Ask-a-Geologist
http://walrus.wr.usgs.gov/docs/ask-a-ge.html/

Association for Women Geoscientists
http://www.awg.org/index.html

Association of American Geographers
http://www.aag.org/

Association of Science - Technology Centers
http://www.astc.org/

Aviation Education
http://www.faa.gov/education/

Bill Nye
http://nyelabs.kcts.org/flash_go.html

Botanical Society of America
http://www.botany.org/

Building Big
http://www.pbs.org/wgbh/buildingbig/

Children's Literature in Science
http://www.enc.org/topics/childlit/

Cool Science (Department of Energy)
http://www.fetc.doe.gov/coolscience/index.html

Council of Chief State School Officers
http://www.ccsso.org/

DiscoverSchool
http://school.discovery.com/

Discovery Channel Cams
http://dsc.discovery.com/cams/cams.html

Earth Science Educator
http://esdcd.gsfc.nasa.gov/ESD/edu/

Earthquake Hazards
http://earthquake.usgs.gov/

Ecological Society of America
http://www.sdsc.edu/ESA/esa.htm

Education in Science, Technology, Energy,
Engineering, and Math
http://www.sandia.gov/ESTEEM/home.html

Educational Resources (Department of
Agriculture)
http://www.usda.gov/news/special/edreso.htm

Educational Sites (U.S. Geological Survey)
http://www.usgs.gov/education.html

Eisenhower National Clearinghouse for
Mathematics and Science Education
http://www.enc.org/

Eisenhower National Clearinghouse's Digital
Dozen
http://www.enc.org/weblinks/dd/

Environmental Education (Department of
Interior)
http://www.blm.gov/education/index.html

Environmental Protection Agency Environmental Education Center
http://www.epa.gov/teachers/index.html

EPA Students' and Teachers' Page
http://www.epa.gov/epaoswer/osw/
students.htm

EPA Students and Teachers: Teaching Aids
http://www.epa.gov/epahome/students.htm

ERIC/CSMEE Clearinghouse for Science, Mathematics, and Environmental Education
http://www.ericse.org/

Exemplary Math/Science Projects
http://www.ncrel.org/msc/products/exemplary.htm

Exploratorium
http://www.exploratorium.edu/

GEMS Teacher's Guides
http://www.lhs.berkeley.edu/gems/gemsguides.html

GLOBE Program
http://www.globe.gov/

Hands-On Universe (National Science Foundation)
http://hou.lbl.gov/

History of Science Society
http://depts.washington.edu/hssexec/

History of Science Sourcebook
http://www.fordham.edu/halsall/science/sciencesbook.html

International Council of Associations for Science Education
http://sunsite.anu.edu.au/icase/

Internet Learning Network (Department of Energy)
http://www.getsmarter.org/index.cfm

Inventor's Toolbox
http://www.mos.org/sln/Leonardo/InventorsToolbox.html

Jungle Trekker: Ecological Education
http://www.jungletrekker.com/

Learning Through Collaborative Visualization Project
http://www.covis.nwu.edu/

Learning Web (U.S. Geological Survey)
http://www.usgs.gov/education/

Lemelson Center (Smithsonian Institute)
http://www.si.edu/lemelson/

Lewis Research Center
http://www.lerc.nasa.gov/WWW/K-12/John/K-12_Teacher_Resources.html

Los Alamos National Laboratory
http://www.lanl.gov/external/education/

Mapping the National Parks
http://memory.loc.gov/ammem/gmdhtml/nphtml/nphome.html

Mars Millennium Project
http://www.mars2030.net/

Mars Polar Lander
http://mars.jpl.nasa.gov/msp98/

Mathematical Sciences Education Board
http://www.nas.edu/mseb/mseb.html

Mid-Atlantic Eisenhower Consortium for Mathematics and Science Education
http://www2.rbs.org/

Moonlink
http://www.moonlink.com/

National Academy of Sciences
http://www.nas.edu/

National Academy Press
http://www.nap.edu/

National Aeronautics and Space Administration - Women of NASA
http://quest.arc.nasa.gov/women/

National Aeronautics and Space Administration Education Program
http://education.nasa.gov/

National Aeronautics and Space Administration Oceanography
http://oceans.nasa.gov/

National Aeronautics and Space Administration Science
http://science.nasa.gov/

National Arboretum
http://www.ars-grin.gov/na/

National Association for Biology Teachers
http://www.nabt.org/

National Council of Teachers of Mathematics
http://www.nctm.org/

National Earthquake Information Center
http://wwwneic.cr.usgs.gov/

National Imagery and Mapping Agency SRTM Kids Page
http://www.nima.mil/srtmkids/SRTM.html

National Institute for Science Education
http://www.wcer.wisc.edu/nise/

National Institutes of Health Office of Science Education http://science-education.nih.gov/

National Library of Medicine (National Institutes of Health)
http://www.nlm.nih.gov/

National Marine Sanctuary
http://www.sanctuaries.nos.noaa.gov/welcome.html

National Museum of Natural History Educational Resources
http://www.mnh.si.edu/edu_resources.html

National Network for Science and Technology
http://www.ets.uidaho.edu/4-H/nnst/

National Oceanographic & Atmospheric Administration (NOAA) Education Website
http://www.education.noaa.gov/

National Research Council
http://www.nas.edu/nrc/

National Science Center (Department of the Army)
http://www.nationalsciencecenter.org/

National Science Education Standards
http://www.nap.edu/readingroom/books/nses/

National Science Foundation - Education
http://www.nsf.gov/home/ehr/start.htm

National Science Foundation
http://www.nsf.gov/

National Science Foundation Science Odyssey
http://www.pbs.org/wgbh/aso/

National Science Foundation Systemic Initiatives
http://www.ehr.nsf.gov/ehr/esr/index.htm

National Science Teachers Association
http://www.nsta.org/

National Science Teachers Association Scope, Sequence, and Curriculum
http://gsh.lightspan.com/nsta/index.htm

National Sciences Resource Center
http://www.si.edu/nsrc/

Newton's Apple
http://www.pbs.org/ktca/newtons/

North American Association for Environmental Education
http://www.naaee.org/

Nova
http://www.pbs.org/wgbh/nova/

Nuclear Regulatory Commission Public
Participation and School Programs
http://www.nrc.gov/NRC/public.html

Observatorium
http://observe.ivv.nasa.gov/nasa/entries/
entry_5.html

Ocean Planet (Smithsonian Institution)
http://seawifs.gsfc.nasa.gov/
ocean_planet.html

Office of Transportation Technologies KIDS'
Page
http://www.ott.doe.gov/kids.html

One Sky, Many Voices
http://groundhog.sprl.umich.edu/

Park Geology - Teacher Features
http://www2.nature.nps.gov/grd/edu/index.htm

Park Geology Tour — Geologic Features
http://www2.nature.nps.gov/grd/tour/

Particle Adventure
http://particleadventure.org/

Paso Partners — Integrating Mathematics,
Science and Language
http://www.sedl.org/scimath/pasopartners/

Plants and Animals in U.S. National Parks
http://www.nps.gov/interp/haycock/
haycock.htm

Profiles in Science
http://www.profiles.nlm.nih.gov/

Project FeederWatch
http://birds.cornell.edu/pfw/

Project Integration and Visualization Tool
http://www.umich.edu/~pbsgroup/PIViT.html

Project Oceanography
http://www.marine.usf.edu/pjocean/

Pulse of the Planet
http://www.pulseplanet.com/

Quest Project - Internet in the Classroom
http://quest.arc.nasa.gov/

Ranger Rick Cool Tours
http://www.nwf.org/kids/cool/

Remote Access Online Real-time Science
Experiment
http://www.cbt.virginia.edu/Olh/

School Science and Mathematics Association
http://www.ssma.org/

Science Activities at Home
http://www.ed.gov/pubs/parents/Science/
Home.html

Science and Nature for Kids
http://kidscience.about.com/kids/kidscience/
index.htm

Science Demonstrations (N.E.R.D.S.)
http://www.theteachersguide.com/
Sciencedemos1.htm

Science Fair Resources
http://www.us.net/mccpta/science.html

Science Information Infrastructure and The
Science Education Gateway
http://ceps.nasm.edu:2020/SII/SII.html

Science Learning Network
http://www.sln.org/

Science Lesson Plans
http://www.lessonplanspage.com/Science.htm

Science Netlinks
http://www.sciencenetlinks.com/index.html

Science Service: Science Resource
http://www.sciserv.org/isef/teacher/resourc.asp

Sharing a World of Resources
http://www.nps.gov/interp/nasa/

Smithsonian Education
http://educate.si.edu/

St. Louis Children's Aquarium
http://www.stlchildrensaquarium.com/

Students' Cloud Observations On-Line
(S'COOL)
http://asd-www.larc.nasa.gov/SCOOL/

Summit on Science
http://www.summitscience.org/

TeacherSource
http://www.pbs.org/teachersource/

This Dynamic Earth: The Story of Plate
Tectonics
http://pubs.usgs.gov/publications/text/
dynamic.html

To Know Ourselves
http://www.ornl.gov/hgmis/publicat/tko/
index.html

Triangle Coalition for Science and Technology
Education
http://www.triangle-coalition.org/

U.S. Global Change Data and Information
System (GCDIS)
http://globalchange.gov/

United States Department of Education
http://www.ed.gov/index.html

Virtual Nuclear Tourist
http://www.nucleartourist.com/

Virtual Vacationland
http://www.bigelow.org/virtual/

Visible Human Project
http://www.nlm.nih.gov/research/visible/
visible_human.html

Volcano World
http://volcano.und.nodak.edu/

Water Resources - Education Resources
http://water.usgs.gov/education.html

Water Science for Schools (U.S. Geological
Survey)
http://ga.water.usgs.gov/edu/index.html

Weather Channel
http://www.weather.com/

Whelmer's
http://www.mcrel.org/whelmers/

Why Files
http://whyfiles.org/

Wildlife Management Activity Guide for
Teachers
http://www.nps.gov/piro/wl_lesns.htm

Wind Resource Database
http://www.nrel.gov/wind/database.html

Your Place in Time: 20th Century America
http://www.hfmgv.org/museum/ypit/index.html

Why Join the National Science Teachers Association?

Whether you are new to the science teaching profession or have many years of classroom experience, NSTA will enrich your teaching and keep you energized.

Here are ways you will enjoy the many benefits of NSTA:

- ➤ Receive idea-packed journals and a newspaper
- ➤ Get discounts on books and classroom materials
- ➤ Participate in outstanding professional development programs
- ➤ Network with colleagues from around the country
- ➤ Receive support on standards, assessment, and inquiry-based learning
- ➤ Discover ways to integrate technology into teaching
- ➤ Win awards for yourself and your students
- ➤ Access our members-only Web resources
- ➤ Hone your teaching skills and learn science content
- ➤ Be recognized as a leader for science education in your school and community
- ➤ Grow, learn, connect — make a BIG impact on what your kids learn!

National Science Teachers Association Mission Statement

The mission of the National Science Teachers Association is to promote excellence and innovation in science teaching and learning for all.

National Science Teachers Association Publications

Below is a sample of publications available from the NSTA Store Online (http://store.nsta.org/)

NSTA Pathways to the Science Standards (Elementary)
NSTA Pathways to the Science Standards (Middle)
College Pathways to the Science Education Standards
Professional Development Planning and Design
Science for All Celebrating Cultural Diversity
Science Educator's Guide to Assessment
Learning English Through Science
Dig In! Hands-On Soil Investigations
Charging Ahead: An Introduction to Electromagnetism
The Life Cycle of Everyday Stuff
Classroom Creature Culture: Algae to Anoles
Science by Design: Construct-a-Boat

Join or Renew Your Membership in NSTA

1. Select the journal you would like to receive as part of your membership:

❑ *Science & Children*, Grades K–8, 8 issues/year
❑ *Science Scope*, Grades 5–9, 8 issues/year
❑ *The Science Teacher*, Grades 7–12, 9 issues/year
❑ *Journal of College Science Teaching*, 7 issues/year

2. Check membership options below:

❑ I have been a Member in the past.
❑ I am renewing, my Member I.D. number is: _____

Special Memberships–

❑ Student, $30/yr. Includes one journal. For full-time students only. Include current registration proof with your payment. Instructor must sign here: _____

❑ 1st-year teacher, $30/yr. Includes one journal. Send a copy of your teaching certificate or a letter (official letterhead) from your administrator.

Regular Memberships–

❑ Membership with one journal, $65/yr.*
❑ with 2 different journals, $95/yr.*
❑ with 3 different journals, $125/yr.*
❑ with 4 different journals, $155/yr.*

Name _____

Address _____

City _____ State _____ Zip+4 _____

Daytime Telephone _____

Fax _____ e-mail _____

3. Payment Method—Canadian and international members, please add $10 per journal per year. (U.S. Dollars)

❑ My check, payable to NSTA, is enclosed.
❑ Please charge my credit card:
　　❑ NSTA MasterCard** ❑ MasterCard ❑ Visa ❑ Discover

Card # _____

Expiration Date _____ Signature _____

4. Mail, Phone, or Fax

NSTA, P.O. B0X 90214, Washington, DC 20090-0214
Phone: 800-722-NSTA, Fax: 703-841-5114

*Membership dues are subject to change.
**Use of this card supports the science teaching profession. Call 800–847–7378 for more Information.